WORKS OF
CROATIAN LATINISTS
Recorded in the British Library
General Catalogue

To Ante and Adrienne with very
best wishes.
Bombay Avenue, Toronto, 6 June 1999
Branko

The tilte-page of Faust Vranèiæ's *Machinae novae* (Venice, 1620)

Front cover: The title-page of Patricius' *Nova de universis philosophia* (Venice,1593)

WORKS
of
CROATIAN LATINISTS

Recorded in the British Library
General Catalogue

SECOND, ENLARGED EDITION

Branko Franolić

CROATIAN INFORMATION CENTRE
Zagreb – London – New York – Toronto – Sydney

Latin as a literary language among the Croats

The universality of Latin in western Europe was due to the fact that it was the only language of culture far into the Middle Ages and a witness to antiquity. It was brought to Croatia in the mid-seventh century as the language of Church liturgy by Roman missionaries and later by various religious orders (Benedictines, Cistercians, etc.) who prayed, taught and wrote in Latin. "The Roman form of Christianity had taken root in the Dalmatian cities in the seventh century and in the Frankish-dominated Croatian hinterland at the turn of the ninth century."[1] By the ninth century Latin had become the language of diplomatic and clerical correspondence (e.g. Pope John VIII's letter to Duke Branimir, 7 June 879).

In the late Middle Ages, clerical documents (e.g. The Proceedings of the Synod of Split; after 917) and books (e.g. Večenega's Gospel Book, Zadar, 1096; kept in the Bodleian Library) were written in Latin. Latin was also used in royal charters (e.g. Petar Krešimir IV's charters of 1066 and 1069, the Golden Bull of King Andrija II, 1222, the fundamental law of the Croatian constitution); in the records of international agreements (e.g. *Pacta Conventa*, 1102); and in the minutes of the sessions of the Croatian parliament (e.g. Zagreb, 20 April 1273). It was the official language of the Croatian parliament (*Sabor*) until 23 October 1847. Many medieval notarial documents (e.g. Zadar, 1146), municipal statutes (e.g. Split, 1240) and chronicles were also written in Latin (e.g. the finest medieval chronicle *Historia Salonitana*, produced by Thomas Archidiaconus in the mid-thirteenth century).

The first Benedictine monasteries, established in Croatia during the 9th century, became, in the 13th century, centres of learning in which the syllabus of *septem artes liberales* was taught. Meanwhile, schools

---

[1] E. Hösch, *The Balkans*, Faber and Faber, London, 1972, p. 64.

run by the Dominicans and Franciscans, in which Latin was the language of instruction, were also opened in the 13th century. Thus the Dominican monastery in Dubrovnik, founded in 1225/6, soon became the focal point of learning, while in 1396 the Dominican General School for the whole province of Dalmatia was founded in Zadar. In 1495 this college was raised to the status of a General College (university) for members of the Dominican Order and laymen who met the required qualifications, and so became the highest establishment of instruction in Croatia.

Croatian Dominicans were often trained in Paris and on their return to Croatia, applied the educational methods which they had learnt abroad to their own teaching. Thus, the Dominican Augustin Kažotić (1260/62-1323) from Trogir who studied in Paris and later became the bishop of Zagreb (1303-1322) reorganized the cathedral school in his diocese using the experience and knowledge he had acquired during his stay in Paris. He established the Zagreb Cathedral School with departments of liberal arts and theology based upon the model of the Dominican *studia sollemnica*.

While Dominicans studied mostly in Paris, Franciscans frequented, from the 13th century, their own school in Oxford. Several manuscripts written by Croatian Franciscans who studied at Oxford are preserved in the Bodleian Library; an example being a text of 1385 by Petar, a Franciscan from Trogir (*Canonici Miscellanea* 525.f.203), which describes the experimental works on parabolic mirrors by Roger Bacon.

One should also mention the astronomical calendar produced in 1291/3 in Zadar, a sole copy of which survives in the Bodleian Library (MS.Ashmoleum 360). The calendar contains a medieval set of tables for astronomical and calendrical calculations (computus) using Arabic numerals, which indicates that the reckoning of dates in Croatia followed West European models. On the other hand, a rare copy of the 14th century manuscript entitled *Secretum philosophorum*, produced by an anonymous English author, probably at Oxford, was brought to Zadar and is kept in the library of the Franciscan monastery.

From the fourteenth century Latin was increasingly used as a literary language. The Catholic faith and the pervasive influence of Italian Humanism both contributed to the constant use of Latin for cultural and administrative purposes. During the age of Humanism and the Renaissance, Latin became the language of literature and science and of the educated elite. Moreover, before the invention of the printing press, which led to the promotion of national languages and the emergence of vernacular literatures, Latin, as an international language with a long tradition and universal currency, hindered the progress of Croatian national literature in the vernacular.

One of the earliest Croatian Latinists was Joannes de Ragusio (Ivan Stojković, 1390/95-1443), a Dominican friar from Dubrovnik (Ragusa) who graduated in theology and philosophy in Paris (1420) and spent most of his life abroad. Dominican Order Procurator and professor at the University of Paris from 1422, he distinguished himself at the Church Council at Basle (1431-1439) with his inaugural speech and interventions against Hussite doctrine. In 1440 he was elevated to Cardinalship by the antipope Felix V. He died in Lausanne in 1443. His original work *Concordantiae Partium sive dictionum indeclinabilium totius Bibliae*, completed and edited by Joannes de Segovia was published in Basle (1496)

Among Latin incunabula, the earliest work by a Croat is the funeral oration *Oratio in funere Reverendissimi Domini D. Petri Cardinalis Sancti Sixti habita,* delivered by Bishop Nicolas of Modruš for Cardinal Pietro Riario, the nephew of the Pope. This work was printed in six editions between 1473 and 1482 in Venice and Padua. Bishop Nicolas was a contemporary of the Latin poet Janus Pannonius, very well known in the history of Humanism. Born in 1434 near Čazma in the Croatian-Hungarian borderland, he died at the castle of Medvedgrad, near Zagreb, in the year 1478. He was one of the followers of the scholar Guarinus of Verona and was on friendly terms with several famous representatives of the Italian Renaissance, especially Pope Pius II, who appointed him, at the age of twenty-six, Bishop of Pécs (Fünfkirchen) in Hungary. Janus, the nephew of the Royal Chancellor Johannes Vitéz (1408-1472), a distinguished Latin orator, spent most of his life at the Italophile court of King Matthias Corvinus (1458-1490) of Hungary in Buda, among a comparatively wide circle of his Croatian compatriots, who zealously and successfully encouraged the intellectual efforts of the king. Janus's work, notably his poetic works, *Panegyrica*, *Elegiarum* and *Epigrammata*, were not printed until after his death in 1478 and carried his name and glory to wider spheres.

More than five hundred years ago, around 1480, Juraj Šižgorić (Georgius Sisgoreus), Canon of Šibenik, one of the earliest Latin authors in Dalmatia, wrote *De situ Illyriae et civitate Sibenici* (1487). This work, which was never printed, contains an interesting description of physical geography of Croatia under the name Illyria and ends with a glorification of Šibenik. It is in this work that one finds the chapter *"De moribus quibusdam Sibenici"* (Concerning some popular customs of Šibenik), in which the author, in translating traditional proverbs from Croatian into Latin, states that he finds them wiser than the laws of Solon and the Sentences of Numa; wiser too than the theorems of Pythagoras. He found the dirges (songs) of the people more moving than the lamentations of Thetis for Achilles, and the wedding songs more beautiful than the epithalamia of Catullus. The love songs which amorous young men used to sing at night seemed to him in no way inferior to those of the refined Tibullus, the flattering Propertius, or the poetess Sappho.

Folk songs and Croatian customs emerging from the depths of the most distant past were the foundation stone of the earliest Croatian literature. Later various external influences stimulated Croatian literature, which soon mirrored philosophical movements seen in western Europe. Yet the echo of the tragic plight of the Croatian people, threatened by the Turks who were making deep inroads into Croatia, continued to reverberate and predominate in their literature for a long time to come, thus making anti-Turkish propaganda the main theme of Croatian Humanist literature. Here was the sombre epic of their painful struggle and their agony resulting from repeated assaults by the Turks over centuries.

Juraj Šižgorić, in addition to the works already mentioned and others which survive only in manuscript, had printed a volume of poetry entitled *Georgii Sisgorei Sibenicensis Dalmatae: Elegiarum et carminum libri tres* (Venetis, per Adam de Rodueil, 1477), the oldest printed collection of poems by a Croatian Latinist. Prior to this work, his long poem *Ad Christum Dominum nostrum eadeq. Virgine gloriosa epigrammata* had appeared in a collection around 1475.

A whole series of Latin works on moral philosophy and theology was written at this time by the Franciscan Juraj Dragišić, Archbishop of Nazareth, better known by his Latin name Georgius Benignus de Salviatis. He was born at Srebrenica in eastern Bosnia around 1445 and died in Italy in 1520. As a child, while taking refuge in Dubrovnik during a Turkish invasion of Bosnia, he found asylum in a Franciscan convent, an order which he was later to enter himself. He continued his studies in Italy and completed them in Paris and Oxford. He was very gifted and was highly esteemed as teacher and priest at the court of Urbino and that of Lorenzo de' Medici in Florence. His defence of Pico della Mirandola, the most brilliant Italian mind of the period, and later of Savonarola, and his support for the great German Humanist Johann Reuchlin have made him famous. Of his works the following have been printed, mostly in Florence and Venice: *Dialectica Nova* (1488 and 1520), *Septem et septuaginta Nicolai de Mirabilibus reperta Mirabilia* (1497), *Opus de natura caelestium spirituum* (1499), and *Defensio praest. viri Joannis Reuchlin* (s.l. 1517). His most important work on logic, *Artis dialecticae praecepta vetera et nova,* was published in Rome (1520).

Among other authors and works of this early period one must also mention Simon Dalmata Pharensis, *Opusculum quo tractatur de baptismo sancti spiritus* (Venetiis, per P. Gallum, 1477); Martin Nimireus Arbensis, *Sermo de passione domini apud div. Alexandrum Pont. Max hab.* (Romae, 1494); and Koriolan Cippico of Trogir, who gave a vivid description of the naval operations against the Turks by the Venetian commander Pietro Mocenigo in *Petri Mocenici imperatoris gestorum libri tres* (Venice, 1477). Cippico's work went into four editions and was translated into Italian three times.

Jacobus Bonus (Bunić) of Dubrovnik was famous for his mythological epic *De raptu Cerberi* (The Capture of Cerberus), a classical allegory depicting Christ's descent into limbo. The poem *De raptu Cerberi libri tres* (s.l. 1500) was dedicated to Cardinal Caraffa. Bunić's long religious epic *De vita et gestis Christi* (*The life and deeds of Christ*, 1526), based on the four Gospels, and describing the whole life of Christ, was published nine years before the famous epic *Christias* (1535) by the Italian Humanist Girolamo Vida.

About 1499, *Elegiarum libellus de laudibus Gnaese puellae* (*A book of elegies in praise of the maiden Agnes*) by Carolus Puteus (Pucić, 1458-1522) of Dubrovnik was printed probably in Florence or Venice. Neither must one forget the work of the Franciscan Benedict Benković of Zadar, *Navigium beate Marie Virginis*, which, according to Pellechet's bibliography of incunabula, appeared *c.*1495, nor his treatise *Scotice subtilitatis Epidicticon*, printed *c.*1520 at Pavia, which was remarkable from a didactic point of view for its explanation of the teaching and work of Duns Scotus. From the hand of Johannes Policarpus Severitanus of Šibenik there appeared between 1494 and 1522 in Rome and Venice several poetic and grammatical works. The Franciscan Thomas Illyricus, an ardent defender of the Roman Catholic faith, worked in France, where he was famous for his learned discussions and defence of Catholicism against Luther. Alongside his *Clypeus Ecclesiae catholicae* (1524), he published other works printed in Toulouse and Turin.

In 1532 there appeared in Venice the work of the Dominican Vincent Priboevus (Pribojević) of Hvar, *Oratio de origine succes-*

sibusque Slavorum, which was filled with national pride and later cited as a formulation of the concept of Panslavism. Ten years later, the eminent historian and Humanist Antun Vrančić (1504-1573) of Šibenik, who became Archbishop of Ostrogon and Primate of all Hungary, published a collection of 41 Latin poems, mainly epigrams, under the title *Otia (Poems of leisure)* in Kraków (1542). Together with the Flemish Humanist Busbecquius, he discovered the famous *Monumentum Ancyranum*, a long inscription in Latin and Greek describing the *Res gestae divi Augusti* (Achievements of the divine Augustus). The inscription is a grave and majestic narrative of the public life and work of Augustus, inscribed on the walls of the temple at Ancyra (modern Ankara). In 1551, four volumes of poetry, *Carmina*, mostly elegies by Ludovicus Pascalis (Paskalić, 1500-1551), were published in Venice. Previously he had also published a collection of Italian poems (*Rime volgari*, Venice, 1549), inspired by Bembo and Petrarch.

The first Latin liturgical books of the bishopric (later the archbishopric) of Zagreb were the *Breviarium Zagrabiense,* printed by Erhard Ratdolt of Augsburg in Venice (1484) and reprinted in the year 1505 by Lucantonio Giunta in Venice, and the beautiful *Missale Almi ep(iscop)atus Zagrabiensis. Impressum Venetiis in aedibus Petri Liechtenstein Coloniensis Germani 1511.* These two works are precious books of the greatest rarity. One must also mention the names of three Croatian printers who in the fifteenth century practised the art of Gutenberg in Italy: Dobrić Dobričević (Boninus de Boninis de Ragusa, 1457-1528) of Lastovo in Dubrovnik district; Andrija Paltašić of Kotor, who worked in Venice (1476-93); and Gregorius Dalmatinus, who also worked in Venice (1482-83).

After the fall of Bosnia (1463) and Hercegovina (1482) to the Turks, the Croat heartlands were left exposed to the Ottoman onslaught. From the mid-fifteenth century, Croatia was repeatedly raided by Turkish forces, culminating in the disastrous defeat of Croatia's nobility at the battle of Krbava in 1493.

The first Croatian Latinist who wrote on Turkish affairs was Felix Petantius (1445-1517) of Dubrovnik. From 1487 to 1490, he was in charge of the calligraphists and miniaturists working at the court of King Matthias Corvinus in Buda, who died in 1490. Matthias's successor Ladislas II sent Felix on diplomatic missions to Dubrovnik, Spain, France, Constantinople and the island of Rhodes. After his return from Rhodes, he wrote three memoirs. In 1502 he presented to the king his first memoir entitled *De itineribus quibus aggrediendi sunt Turci*, which was reprinted fifteen times between 1522 and 1797 and translated into German and Italian. His second memoir, which is a description of the administrative, judicial, financial and military organisation of the Turkish Empire, is preserved in two manuscript versions; one is held in the National Library in Vienna and the second is kept at the National Library in Budapest; it is richly illustrated with numerous "portraits" of Turkish sultans. The third memoir, known as *Historia Turcica*, is held at the Municipal Library in Nuremberg (pressmark Ms Solger 31.2°). It was written in Buda and was beautifully illuminated in the miniaturists' workshop of Matthias Corvinus at the end of 1501. Petantius's account of the affairs of the Turkish state seems to be more objective and comprehensive than the narrative of events and experiences related by his compatriot Bartol Georgijević, who spent nine years in Turkish captivity (1526-35).

As the beginning of the sixteenth century proved so fatal to Croatia, Croatian leaders, in their Latin orations and epistles, appealed in desperation to western rulers for help in their struggle against the Ottoman invaders. Their voice made itself heard above the oppression and dissipation of the Ottomans. They rise before us like bronze columns, bloody witnesses of an inexorable destiny.

Among the printed Latin orations and epistles which have survived, most of which are held in the British Library in London, let us mention *Oratio habita presente Julio II Pont. Opt. Max.* (Romae, 1512). This was delivered by Bernardo Zane, Archbishop of Split, on behalf of Ban (Viceroy) Petar Berislavić, who died in 1520 in a battle against the Turks. Then we have the impressive speech recounting the devastation of Croatia by the Bishop of Modruš, Šimun Benja Kožičić (1460-1536), in the Lateran Council on 27 April 1513, *Simoni Begnae Episcopi Modrusiensis de Croatiae desolatione ad Leonem X Pont. Max.* (Romae, 1516), and also the *Oratio Stephani Possedarski pro Domino Johanne Torquato . . . defensore Crovacie*, a request made in the name of Ban Ivan Torquat Karlović (1521-25) for weapons to defend Croatia, and for priests to encourage and console the people in their despair at the aggression.

In 1522, Count Bernardinus de Frangepanibus (1453-1529), a survivor of the battle of Krbava, delivered a distressing address to the State Senate in Nuremberg, *Oratio pro Croatia, Nurenbergae in Senatu Principum Germaniae habita,* imploring western potentates for help. Bernardinus was one of the most distinguished members of the family of Frankapans, which had been linked for centuries with the destiny of Croatia. He concluded his appeal by quoting Horace: "Et tua res agitur, paries quum proximus ardet" ("You are concerned when your neighbour's house is burning").

Almost at the same time the oration delivered in the presence of the Pope by Bernardinus's heroic son, Christopher (1482-1527), left the press. He had become famous by virtue of his strange destiny, and the several years he spent in captivity in Venice. The Danish art historian, Henry Thode, dedicated his admirable book *Frangipani's ring, an event in the life of Henry Thode* (published by John Macqueen, London, 1900) to the memory of Christopher.

Only one copy of his *Oratio ad Adrianum Sextum Pont. Max. Christophori de Frangepanibus Veg. Seg. Modrusieque Comitis* (Paris, 1523?) has survived, and it is held by the British Library. Christopher had added to his oration a memorial, which begins: "Holy Father! the counts, barons, nobles and people of the kingdom of Croatia, addressed themselves to my lord and father speaking thus, 'You who are the oldest and mightiest among us must zealously put our case to our Holy Father the Pope and to the apostolic Holy See

13

and to Christian Princes and Kings. Tell them with what ills, miseries, and anguish the Turks torture and torment us, how in overrunning our country they forcibly drag us into cruel captivity, how abandoned by all we are compelled either to leave our homes and to wander abroad, and to make our way by begging through the world, or to conclude a treaty with the Turks and serve them if the protection and help of His Holiness is denied to us'".

Another member of the family of Frankapans, Count Vuk, Ban of Croatia and Dalmatia, spoke at the Diet of Augsburg in 1530: *Oratio ad Carolum V . . . ac ad . . . principes Romani imperii, facta ex parte regnicolarum Croatiae, 24 Aug. 1530 habita* (Augustae Vindelicorum, 1530). His moving speech, full of pathos, appeared simultaneously in the Latin original and a German translation. He declared that little Croatia had defended herself single-handedly for eighty years, but that now she would be compelled to surrender to superior forces unless help arrived soon. He himself fell in the battle of Schmalkalden in 1546.

The peripatetic Humanist, Tranquillus Andreis (Andronicus Andrijević, 1490-1571), offered persuasive warnings, and tirelessly urged the Christian states to unite against the Turkish peril, which was becoming more and more threatening every day. He was born in Trogir in Dalmatia, and was descended from a family of old nobility. He had studied in Italy and was a keen Humanist who lectured on Cicero and Quintilian, among others, at the University of Leipzig.

It was in Leipzig that he had his *Oratio de laudibus eloquentiae* printed (1518). At Erfurt he was saluted in a dithyrambic poem by Eobanus Hessus, the king of the German Latin poets. Among the letters of Erasmus of Rotterdam there can be found a long message addressed to him. Later, Andrijević took up diplomacy, serving as secretary and ambassador to the court of the Grand Sultan and to the French, English, Polish and Valachian courts. He served first under Francis I of France, then under the Hungaro-Croatian King Ivan Zapolya, and finally under Ferdinand I of Austria and Charles V.

Amongst Andrijević's published works are *Ad Deum contra Thurcas Oratio carmine heroico* (1518), and, dating from the time of the Diet of Augsburg, *Oratio contra Thurcas ad Germanos habita* (Augsburg, 1518). In 1545 he published *Ad Optimates Polonos admonita* (Cracouiae, 1545). Eduard Böcking sang his praises in his edition of the works of Ulrich von Hutten, and reprinted his writings on the Turks. During this same period, Marko Marulić (1450-1524) of Split was active. He was a Humanist of worldwide fame who, although a layman, devoted his life to religious contemplation and to the moral improvement of his fellow man, notably his fellow citizens. By the beginning of the sixteenth century we come across the first secular work of Croatian literature, *Istoria svete udovice Judit (The History of the Holy Widow Judith)*, by Marko Marulić. This first Croatian epic, which tells the biblical story of Judith and the slaying of Holofernes, was published in five editions between 1521 and 1627. The story of the Apocryphal book of Judith, which is included in the Roman Catholic Vulgate, proved extremely popular with a wide cross-section of the population in the Croatian version. It was particularly popular with women and girls, untrained in Latin, who were greatly attached to their native tongue. In the preface to his *Judit*, Marulić writes: "In reading this history I was minded to translate it into our [Croatian] tongue, so that it might be understood by those who are not learned in Latin or clerical writing."

The ethical message of Judith "appears to be a call for Christian faith and unity in the struggle with the Turks who are clearly paralleled with Holofernes. . . . By its very popularity, *Judita* suggests an attempt to create a literary work which would arouse the self-consciousness of Marulić's own countrymen and give them a sense of identity. . . . In this first Croatian epic, Marulić embodied an urgent call to his own people to hold firm to the ideals of Christendom which alone could give them the moral force to withstand the Turkish peril."[2]

As the culture of some Croatian Humanists was bilingual or even trilingual, they used to write in Latin, Croatian or Italian. Thus, a characteristic feature of Croatian Humanist literature, shared by Humanism throughout Europe, was the parallel development of Latin and vernacular literature.

Marulić also wrote under the Latin form of his name, as was the custom of the time. As Marcus Marulus Spalatensis, he was well-known as the author of a series of works of religious morality written in Latin, some of which were highly regarded: *De Institutione bene beateque vivendi per exempla sanctorum* (1st edn., 1498), *Evangelistarium* (1487), *Dialogus de laudibus Herculis* (1524), and other noteworthy works in poetry, history and archaeology, most of which were published in several editions, as well as being translated into German, Italian, French, Czech and Portuguese. In the sixteenth century Marulić's *De Institutione* went into seventeen editions, published in major cities such as Venice, Antwerp, Basle, Cologne, and Paris. It was translated into five languages, and these translations went into forty-five editions.

A Japanese adaptation of *De Institutione (Sanctos no gosayuno)* came out in Nagasaki in 1595. Moreover, *De Institutione* served as a vade-mecum to St Francis Xavier on his missions to India. In 1577 the English Catholic printer John Fowler of Bristol, by then in exile in Antwerp, published *M. Maruli dictorum libri sex (De Instituione)*.

Evangelistarium was printed six times during Marulić's lifetime; unfortunately, not a single copy of the 1487, 1500 and 1515 editions has been found so far. In 1529, a copy of *Evangelistarium* became a bedside book of Henry VIII, who entered annotations in his own hand. In 1585-87 Sir Philip Howard, Earl of Arundel, while imprisoned in the Beauchamp Tower within the Tower of London, occupied himself by translating into English Marulić's Latin poem as

[2] E. D. Goy, "Marko Marulić", *BC Review*, No. 13, Oct. 1977, pp. 7-8.

A Dialogue Betwixt a Christian and Christ Hanging on the Cross (thirty-nine four-line stanzas).

Marulić's considerable opus includes the beautiful and lofty *Epistola ad Adrianum VI Pont. Max. De calamitatibus occurrentibus, et exhortatio ad communem omnium Christianorum Unionem et Pacem* (Romae, per Bern. De Vitalibus, 1522). This epistle is an impressive exhortation to resist the Turkish invader.

The eminent French scholar, Charles Béné, whose seminal work *Erasme et Saint Augustin* (Geneva, 1969) is one of the landmark books in the history of Humanism, placed Marulić alongside the great figures of European Humanism.

In 1526, after the defeat of the young Jagellon, Louis II, at the battle of Mohács, the greater part of the kingdom of Hungary was annexed by the Turks, who reached the gates of Vienna in 1529. At the same battle, a young Croatian scholar, Bartol Georgijević was taken prisoner by the Turks, and deported as a slave to Turkey, where he served seven different masters over several years of captivity. Georgijević's mother tongue, Croatian, was very useful in Turkey, and, according to him, Sultan Suleiman II knew and esteemed the language. Besides Croatian, Georgijević also spoke Hungarian, Latin, Greek, Turkish, Arabic and Hebrew.

While still in captivity, he spent some time in Armenia, and taught Greek in Damascus, before he succeeded in escaping to Jerusalem in 1535. He took service in the Franciscan monastery there and found refuge until 1537. In 1538 he fulfilled a vow by undertaking pilgrimages to Santiago de Compostella, and in 1544 he went to The Netherlands and Germany, and later to France and Italy as "peregrinus Hierosolymitanus".

Georgijević published a series of books in Latin, *De Turcorum moribus epitome* (Antwerp, 1544), describing the fate awaiting Christian prisoners. Also in 1544, he published *De afflictione tam captivorum . . .* (Antwerp, 1544), a further description of the distressing plight of Christians held in Turkish captivity, with fragments in the

Croatian language, and *De ritibus differentiis Graecorum et Armeniorum*. In 1545 he published *Epistola exhortatoria contra infideles*, an exhortation to war against the Turks, and *Prognoma sive praesagium Mehemetanorum*, a prophecy of the decadence of Turkey. From 1544 until his death in Rome in 1566, Georgijević produced many books on Turkish ways, customs, religion, and ceremonies, as well as on the miserable state of the Christians in Turkish bondage. In his various works on Turkish affairs, he implored, harangued and urged European rulers and religious leaders to attack the advancing Turks. His books about the Turks and their Christian captives, his history of the Turkish sultans, and his description of his own journey to Jerusalem were read with great interest all over Europe, and found a favourable response in intellectual circles. He was helped by Philipp Melanchthon and Martin Luther, not to mention Charles V, Emperor of the Holy Roman Empire, Maximilian II, Sigismund II of Poland, the Popes Julius III and Pius V, and other influential figures. His works were translated into French, German, Flemish, Italian, Czech, Polish and English. Georgijević's work as translated into English by Hugh Goughe was printed by Thomas Marsche, and published in London (1570) under the title *The ofspring of the house of Ottomano, and officers pertaining to the greate Turkes Court*.

Georgijević's books created a sensation in his time because of their unique subject matter and presentation. No Croatian Humanist was more widely read in Europe than him. The British Library in London holds 44 copies of Georgijević's various works.

A dramatic description of the battle of Mohács was given by Stjepan Brodarić (1471-1539) in his monograph *Clades in campo Mohacz* (1568), which went into eight editions, while the brilliant stylist Ludovicus Cerva (Crijević) Tuberon (1459-1527) provided another work on the origin, customs and deeds of the Turks, *De Turcarum origine, moribus & rebus gestis commentarius* (Florence, 1590). Crijević's *Commentaria* (*Commentaries*) was put on the Roman Catholic "Index of Prohibited Books" because of its criticism of Church policy, morals and attitudes, and its marked tolerance of other religions and objectivity regarding the Turks.

The most original Croatian philosopher of the Renaissance, Franjo Petrić (F. Patrizi, Patricio), was born on the Adriatic island of Cres in the Gulf of Kvarner, in north-west Croatia, in 1529. He studied at Ingolstadt and read philosophy and humanities at the University of Padua (1547-54). He spent many years in Venice, where a number of his writings were published between 1553 and 1572. He was professor of Platonic philosophy at the University of Ferrara (1579-92), and then at the Collegio della Sapienza in Rome until his death in 1597.

Petrić was a versatile writer, a typical Renaissance *homo universalis*, with interests in many different intellectual fields. He published treatises on history, poetics, rhetoric, literary criticism, metaphysics, ethics, natural philosophy and mathematics, besides translating a number of Greek works into Latin. His major systematic philosophical work *Nova de universis philosophia* (Ferrara, 1591; reprinted in Venice in 1593) is a blend of Platonism and natural philosophy, with a strong anti-Aristotelian bias. Plato's philosophy had a great appeal for Petrić, probably because it attaches great importance to mathematical knowledge. His philosophical and scientific theories are expounded in *Della nuova geometria* and *De rerum natura libri II* (both published in Ferrara in 1587).

"Patrizi's importance in the history of science rests primarily on his highly original views concerning the nature of space, which have striking similarities to those later developed by Henry More and Isaac Newton."[3] This view is shared by John Christopher Henry, who, in his doctoral thesis "Francesco Patrizi and the concept of space" (defended at the University of Leeds in March 1977), concludes: "Patrizi's works seem to have been widely known throughout Europe and directly influenced some of the Cambridge Platonists, notably Joseph

---

[3] Charles B. Schmitt, *Dictionary of Scientific Biography*,Charles Scribner's Sons, New York, vol. X, p. 416.

Glanville and Henry More. Henry More can be seen as a link between Patrizi and Sir Isaac Newton. Patrizi's long arguments for an isotropic, unchanging, immobile and infinite space, his vehement denunciation of the Aristotelian concept, and his establishment of 'space' as a new philosophical term can finally be said to have taken root when Newton was able to discuss absolute space after writing: 'I do not define space . . . as being well known to all.'" (pp. 167-168).

The wandering, adventurous Humanist and polyhistor, Paul Skalić (1534-1573), published his work *Encyclopaedia seu orbis disciplinarum tam sacrarum quam prophanarum epistemon* (*Encyclopaedia, or Knowledge of the World of Disciplines* . . .) in Basle (1559). Although it is not strictly speaking an encyclopaedic dictionary, but a publication containing "a more heterogeneous collection of essays" (*Encyclopaedia Britannica* (1971), vol. 8, p. 363), it is worth mentioning here since it is "the first work known to contain the word [encyclopaedia] in the title" (cf. *Encyclopedia Americana* (1979), vol. 10, p.330). "Scalich's Encyclopaedia brought the term back into prominence" (*Macmillan Family Encyclopedia*, vol. 7, p.163). Skalić also penned the musical treatise, *Dialogus de Lyra* (Cologne, 1570).

The most prominent Croatian Protestant Humanist, who lived in Germany in the mid-sixteenth century, was the theological controversialist Matthias Flacius Illyricus (1520-1575) of Labin in Istria. He began his Humanist studies at Venice, and later went to Basle, Tübingen and Wittenberg, which was the cradle of Lutheranism. There he came under Martin Luther's influence and became a confirmed Lutheran. He was professor of Hebrew and Greek at Wittenberg University from 1544 to 1549 and led the Gnesio (i.e. legitimate) Lutheran party, which claimed to follow Luther's teachings unmodified.

Flacius wrote a great number of theological pamphlets, arguments and diatribes in Latin. But apart from polemical works, he also wrote *Clavis Scripturae Sacrae* (*Key to Sacred Scripture*, 1567), and *Catalogus testium veritatis* (*Catalogue of Witnesses to the Truth*,

1556), which were pioneering works in Protestant biblical hermeneutics and Protestant historiography. Much of Flacius's fame rests upon the *Ecclesiastica historia* . . ., a complete and well-documented Lutheran version of Church history (Basel 1559-74). This thirteen-volume work, known as the *Magdeburg Centuries*, was produced by a group of Lutheran scholars known as the Centurians of Magdeburg, who worked under the guidance of Matthias Flacius Illyricus. "Flacius's ardent polemics in defense of Luther's message at a time when it was seriously menaced by political and ideological forces contributed much to its preservation, and his intellectual contributions in liturgy, hermeneutics, church history, and dogmatics greatly enriched Protestant orthodoxy"[4].

When in 1541 Flacius came to Tübingen, he stayed with the family of his compatriot Matija Grbić (Matthias Garbitius Illyricus) who was Luther's protégé and Melanchton's disciple. Grbić was professor of Greek literature at Tübingen university (1537-1559) and published several works in this field.

Another theological controversialist and dissident, Marko Antun de Dominis, was born on the Adriatic island of Rab, in north-west Croatia, in 1560. He studied at the University of Padua, and subsequently taught mathematics, logic and philosophy at Verona, Padua and Brescia. In 1596 he left the Society of Jesus to become administrator of the diocese of Senj, and was appointed bishop of the city in 1600. In 1602 de Dominis was appointed Archbishop of Split, a position which automatically made him Primate of Dalmatia and Croatia.

De Dominis became involved in the struggle between the papacy and Venice during the interdict controversy, when the Pope tried to break the resistance of the Venetian clergy to the supreme authority of Rome. His writings on behalf of Venice were censured in Rome, especially when he wrote against the papal secular prerogatives and

---

[4] R. Kolb, "Flacius Illyricus", *The Encyclopedia of Religion*, Macmillan Publishing Company, New York, 1987, vol. 5. p. 348

refuted the secular power of the Church. In 1616, he fled to England, where he was hospitably received. When de Dominis first arrived in England, King James I asked Lancelot Andrewes, Bishop of Winchester, whether the Bishop of Split was a Protestant or not. Bishop Andrewes replied: "Truly, I know not; but he is a Detestant of divers opinions of Rome" (Granger, *A Biographical History of England*, 1824, vol. II, p. 63). Regarding de Dominis as a convert to Anglicanism, James I appointed him Dean of Windsor, and gave him the rich living of West Ildesley in Berkshire. He was also made a Doctor of Divinity by Cambridge University.

In 1617 the first part of de Dominis's main theological work *De republica ecclesiastica* . . . was published in London. Immediately after publication, it became the first book on the Roman "Index". In it, de Dominis asserted that the Pope did not have jurisdiction over bishops, but was *primus inter pares*, and he urged the unity of all Christian churches, and their commitment to exclusively spiritual ends and peace among nations. He also favoured the rights of national churches, and developed a vision of world peace which he opposed to Roman centr ilism. In *De republica ecclesiastica*, de Dominis re- presented himself as a Catholic universalist, bearing the parallel titles of Archbishop of Split and Dean of Windsor. According to his own words, his main concern during his stay in England was to reconcile the Anglican and Roman churches.

When his friend and fellow countryman Gregory XV became Pope, de Dominis decided to leave England, and went to Brussels. While waiting for the Pope's permission to proceed to Rome, de Dominis published *Sui reditus ex Anglia consilium* (1623), in which he denounced the Church of England as a wretched schism and a degraded body. This was a complete recantation of his former tract *Consilium profectionis* . . . (Heidelberg, 1616), in which he explained the reasons of his departure for England and his "flight from Baby- lon". In 1623 he returned to Rome, formally made his recantation, and reconverted to the Church of Rome.

After Gregory XV's death, de Dominis was imprisoned as a relapsed heretic in the Castel Sant' Angelo, where he died soon afterwards. He was posthumously found guilty of heresy. His body and theological books were burned on the Campo di Fiore in Rome on 21 December 1624, and the ashes were thrown into the Tiber. Eight years later, de Dominis's successor at Padua University, Galileo, was also put on trial as a heretic and condemned by the same judge, Cardinal Barberini, who became Pope Urban VIII.

In 1595 the *Dictionarium Quinque Nobilissimarum Europae Linguarum, Latinae, Italicae, Germanicae, Dalmatiae et Ungaricae Fausti Verantii* was published in Venice by Nicolaus Morettus (vi + 128 pp. in-8°). This multilingual dictionary is often regarded as the first major dictionary of the Croatian language and its author, Faust Vrančić (1551-1617), as the father of Croatian lexicography. Vrančić's work undoubtedly represents a landmark in the history of Croatian, and indeed European, lexicography.

At the beginning of the seventeenth century, the first grammar of the Croatian language, Bartol Kašić's *Institutionum linguae Illyricae libri duo,* was printed in Rome (1604). Both Vrančić and Kašić tried to place Croatian vernacular as a standard language on the same level as Latin, to which it was subordinated yet free to develop independently, just as the western European vernaculars were doing.

Among historical works written in Latin in the seventeenth and eighteenth centuries, the foremost is *De Regno Dalmatiae et Croatiae libri sex* by Ivan Lučić (Lucius) of Trogir, the founder of modern Croatian historiography. The title of this work alone is proof of the links created by language and destiny. The first edition was published in 1666 by the famous bookseller Johannes Blaeu in Amsterdam. It is recognised as an excellent and serious work whose composition and development rival the best of its contemporaries. From amongst many works one must mention those of Baron Georgius Rattkay, *(Memoria Regum et Banorum regnorum Dalmatiae, Croatiae et Slavoniae,* Vindobonae, 1652), and Balthasar Adam Krčelić, Canon of Zagreb,

23

(De regnis Dalmatiae, Croatiae, Sclavoniae notitiae praeliminares, Zagrabiae, 1770); and to these can be added a whole series of specialised works.

The distinguished numismatist and palaeographer Anselmo Banduri (1671-1741) of Dubrovnik worked in Italy and France. His monumental four-volume history of Byzantium and its antiquities, *Imperium orientale . . .,* was published in Paris (1711). He was a member of the French *Académie des Inscriptions et Belles-Lettres.*

At the turn of the seventeenth century, Pavao Ritter Vitezović (1652-1713) emerged as "the first builder of political and cultural unity of all Croats" (Franjo Fancev). His great contribution to the progress of intellectual life can scarcely be appreciated in its true light today. Far in advance of his time, he achieved a great deal by creating a secular popular literature in Croatian, by placing his literary activity in the service of the Croatian language in general and by his work in the field of history. His unwavering friendly relationship with the Carniol historian Johann Weickhard Valvasor (1641-1693) is seen in the signs of his evident collaboration in the work of the latter.

Vitezović wrote many works in Croatian and Latin but only a few have been printed. Thus his important Latin-Croatian dictionary (*Lexicon latino-illyricum,* one volume, 1132 pp.) remained in manuscript. In taking over a printing shop that a patriotic Croatian gentleman gave to the nation in 1666, he became the first printer in Zagreb. His activity in the field of heraldry and of political history in Latin was various and characterized by great patriotism and a rare perspicacity. In 1696 he appealed to the estates of the realm of Croatia, asking to be supplied with reproductions of coats of arms and information on families and various regions in view of his plan to publish a work entitled *De Aris et Focis Illyricorum.* The fruits of this appeal appeared in his book of heraldry, *Stemmatographia, Sive Armorum Illyricorum Delineatio, Descriptio, et Restitutio, Authore Ecquite Paulo Ritter,* published in Vienna (1701). Amongst his Latin works one must also cite his historical writing in hexameters,

Plorantis Croatiae saecula duo (*Two Centuries of Grieving Croatia*, 1703), a melancholy versicular description of the Turkish wars in Croatia and an apologia of the greater Croatia, *Croatia rediviva* (*Croatia Reborn*), Zagreb, 1700. These two works show the same "*cruciatus doloris*" (torment of pain) which, two centuries earlier, Šižgorić had said was the inspiration for his poetry. Towards the end of his life there appeared in Trnava, in 1712, his *Bosna captiva*, an expression of his distress that Bosnia remained under Turkish domination and of his desire and hope that Turkey would be fully vanquished. Paul Vitezović was an exceptional man with bold ideas which were still alive more than a hundred years after his death, for they fired with enthusiasm and inspired Ljudevit Gaj (1809-1872), the creator of modern "Illyrianism", whose activity at the time of the Croatian national awakening was that of a pioneer. Vitezović died in 1713, after a troubled life full of privations, in exile in Vienna.

The Franciscan Filip Lastrić (1700-1783), in his *Epitome vetustatum Bosnensis provinciae* (1762), provided a comprehensive history of the Bosnian Franciscan province (*Provincia Bosnae Argentinae*). His bilingual (Latin-Croatian) collection of sermons, *Testimonium bilabium . . .*, was published in Venice (1755). In his treatise *In veterem Croatorum patriam indagatio philologica* (*Philological Research on the Ancient Homeland of the Croats*, Zagreb, 1790), the philologist Matija Petar Katančić (1750-1825) of Valpovo in Slavonia, professor of archaeology at the University of Budapest, claimed that the Croats were the indigenous inhabitants of Pannonia and Dalmatia. His views strongly influenced partisans of the so-called "Illyrian Movement" of the 1830s, who firmly believed the Croats to be direct descendants of the Illyrians. Even more important is his *Specimen philologiae et geographiae . . . in quo de origine, lingua et litteratura Croatorum . . . disseritur* (Zagreb, 1795), in which he credits the Dalmatian writers, especially those of Dubrovnik, with being the founding fathers of Croatian classical literature. A bilingual (Latin-Croatian) collection of Katančić's poetry, containing 47 Latin poems, entitled *Fructus auctumnales* (*Autumnal Fruits*), was published in Zagreb (1791).

Croatian Latinists also translated works from other languages, especially classical Greek, into Latin. Thus Rajmund Kunić (1719-1794) of Dubrovnik, for many years professor of rhetoric and Greek at Rome, translated the *Iliad* (1776), a work which is considered the best Latin translation of Homer's epic. His satirical and love epigrams were published posthumously: *Epigrammatum libri quinque* (Parma, 1803) and *Epigrammata* (Dubrovnik, 1827). The learned Jesuit Kazimir Bedeković (1726-1782), who taught Newton's laws of motion and gravitation at the Zagreb Academy, translated into Latin *Reflexions upon learning* by Thomas Baker, as *Tractatus de incertitudine scientiarum* / orig. *Reflexions upon learning Auctore Thoma Baker. In Academia Zagrabiensi latinitate donatus a Casimir Bedekovich* . . . (Zagrabiae, 1759). He also wrote several religious plays in Latin, *Ioseph* (Vienna, 1778) and *Hilaria ante cineres* (*Merry plays before Ash Wednesday*, Vienna, 1780), depicting the lives of St Bernard and St Justin.

As the international language of science, Latin was the cultural medium par excellence. Early Croatian scientists, following the western European model, made Latin an indispensable part of their means of expression.

Hermann of Dalmatia (*fl.* 1138-43) was an important figure in the transmission of Arabic learning to the west. By 1138 he had settled in Spain and become sufficiently fluent in Arabic to produce nine works, mostly astrological translations from Arabic into Latin. He translated the astrological treatise *Fatidica* (1138) written by Sahl ibn Bishr, Abu Ma'šar's introduction to astronomy (*Introductorium in astronomiam*, 1140) and Al Khwârizmî's astronomical tablets (1140-1143). He produced a Latin edition of Ptolemy's *Planisphere* from the Arabic translation of the Greek original, the only extant version of this astronomical treatise, and a version of Euclid's *Elements*. In 1143 Hermann completed his only independent work of philosophy, *De*

Essentiis, in which his view of the fundamental elements of the universe shows the strong influence of the Platonic school of Chartres. Hermann's *De Essentiis* was copied several times during the Middle Ages; of the three copies extant to date, in Naples, London and Oxford, one is held by the British Library manuscript collections.

Federico Grisogono (1472-1538) of Zadar studied medicine and philosophy at Padua. After receiving a doctorate from the University of Padua (1506), he taught there for a while and then in 1508 he returned to Zadar, where he practised medicine and made astronomical observations. In his work *De modo collegiandi, prognosticandi et curandi febres, nec non de humana felicitate, ac denique de fluxu et refluxu maris* (Venice, 1528) Grisogono solved the problem of the tides in the special section entitled *Tractatus de occulta causa fluxus et refluxus maris*. The problem of the second daily tide was one of the most difficult problems of his time, and Grisogono's solution showed the influence of the fourteenth-century Italian scientist Jacopo Dondi. He argued that the tides result from the combined action of the sun and the moon. He also constructed a mathematical model which predicted the high tide quite accurately.

Marko Antun de Dominis (1560-1624), while teaching mathematics at Padua, wrote two works on physics. The first one, *De radiis, visus et lucis in vitris perspectivis et iride* (Venice, 1611), deals with geometrical optics and the theory of the rainbow. It is apparently the first treatise to point out that in the phenomenon of the rainbow the light undergoes two refractions and an intermediate reflection in each raindrop. In the second, *Euripus seu de fluxu et refluxu maris sententia* (Rome, 1624), de Dominis is concerned with tides. He believed that the moon and the sun influence the sea in a manner analogous to a magnet. He adopted and corrected Grisogono's theory of a second daily tide caused by the influence of both bodies in any position.

The first to apply Galilean principles of measurement to biological matters was Santorio Santorio (1561-1636) from Istria, called Sanctorius. He obtained his doctor's degree at the University of Padua

(M.D. 1582). Invited to attend as physician on a leading Croat nobleman, probably Count Zrinski, he spent twelve years in practice in Croatia, from 1587 to 1599, mostly on the Adriatic coast. In October 1611 Sanctorius was appointed professor of medical theory at the University of Padua (1611-24) and during the rest of his life he experimented unceasingly. In 1612 Sanctorius published a work in which he described a thermometer to measure body temperature. This work was a commentary on Galen's *Art of Medicine*. His experiments, conducted with a balance, a pulse clock and other measuring instruments, lasted over thirty years, and in 1614 he published the results of his research in a series of aphorisms entitled *De statica medicina*. This famous book went through many editions and was translated into the major European languages. His experiments laid the foundations of the modern study of metabolism.

Although Faust Vrančić, who studied philosophy and law at Padua (1568-70), was principally a man of letters and spent most of his career as a diplomat, administrator and ecclesiastic, he also studied mechanics and mathematics in his leisure time. In 1616, he published a treatise on logic (*Logica nova*, Venice, 1616) and wrote an important folio volume entitled *Machinae novae* (Venice, 1620?). In *Machinae novae* Vrančić illustrates five different types of horizontal mills (pls, XIII, XII, XI, IX, VIII). Three out of the five illustrations show gear-arm construction, with four arms crossing each other to form at the centre a square through which the main shaft passes. These illustrations of Vrančić are the earliest examples of the improved clasp-arms wheels in windmills. How many of these early designs were actually put into practice is not known. Vrančić is renowned in the history of technology as the author of *Machinae novae*. Although some of his "machines" were not wholly original, they were nevertheless explained in print for the first time. A particularly interesting section entitled *"Homo volans"* includes the first published mention of a parachute.

The mathematician and physicist Marin Getaldić (1566-1626) of

Dubrovnik lived the peripatetic life of a scholar. He lived in Italy, France, England, Germany and Belgium. During his stay in Paris he was particularly influenced by François Viète, with whom he associated. Getaldić wrote in Latin and his works were widely known. Archimedes and especially Apollonius were his inspiration. His first work, *Promotus Archimedis* (Rome, 1603), dealt with the famous problem of the crown. In it he theoretically explained the method of determining the specific gravity of solid bodies. His works on mathematics and geometry can be divided into two different groups. The first group consists of works published during his life: *Supplementum Apollonii Galli* (Venice, 1607), *Apollonius redivivus* (Venice, 1607), *Apollonius redivivus, liber secundus* (Venice, 1613), and *Variorum problematum collectio* (Venice, 1607). In all these works Getaldić solves geometric problems by Euclidean methods. His last work, published posthumously, *De resolutione et compositione mathematica* (Rome, 1630), constitutes the second group in which Getaldić applies consistently the so-called algebraic (Viète's) method of analysis.

Getaldić's contemporary Georgius Raguseus (1579-1622) from Dubrovnik taught philosophy at the university of Padua (1601-1622) as a rival and successor to Cesare Cremonini. In his main philosophical work *Peripateticae Disputationes . . .* (Venice, 1613), he defends the peripatetic Aristotelian approach of thinking in particulars and scientific deductions in opposition to the metaphysical speculation of Platonism. In a collection of his letters entitled *Epistolarum mathematicarum seu de divinatione libri duo*, published in Paris (1623), he criticizes divinatory astrology and censures magic and cabbala. In 1837, the British Library acquired the manuscript by Georgius Raguseus entitled *Epistolae Morales, dialecticae et mathematicae*. (Se. XVII. Folio, 10.810)

Matija Frkić (1583-1669), a Conventual monk from the island of Krk, who in 1628 was appointed professor of metaphysics at Padua university produced a number of theological works in which he deals with metaphysical and theological problems. However, his *De*

29

Caelesti substantiae . . . (Venice, 1646) is of particular interest because he occupies himself with the philosophical and physical problems of natural philosophy.

Another polyhistor from Dubrovnik, Stjepan Gradić (1613-1683), during his stay in Rome (1642-83), moved in the political and scholarly circles of Pope Alexander VII and Queen Christina of Sweden. He was the custodian and, by the end of his life, the head of the Vatican Library. His work *Peripateticae philosophiae pronunciata disputationibus proposita* (s.a., s.l.) is a systematic review of logic, scholastic philosophy and Aristotle's natural philosophy. In his second work, *Dissertationes physico-mathematicae quatuor* (Amsterdam, 1680), he follows Galileo's scientific method of observation and direct evidence. He also deals with the natural causes of motion and the laws of acceleration and falling bodies.

The most fervent follower and proponent in Europe of the "new natural philosophy" (Newton's laws of motion and gravitation) was Ruđer Bošković. Born in Dubrovnik in 1711, he entered the Society of Jesus and passed his novitiate in Rome at the Collegium Romanum, where, in 1735, he began studying Newton's *Opticks* and *Principia*. In 1740, he became professor of mathematics at the Collegium Romanum. Bošković continually promoted international cooperation in geodesy (large-scale measurements of the earth, allowing for its curvature). He collaborated enthusiastically with an English colleague, Christopher Maire, Rector of the English Jesuit College in Rome, in measuring an arc of two degrees of the meridian between Rome and Rimini. This onerous task took three years, and the report on it came out in Rome at the end of 1755.

Bošković's magnum opus, *Philosophiae naturalis theoria redacta ad unicam legem virium in natura existentium*, was published in Vienna in 1758. A bilingual Latin-English edition was published in Chicago and London in 1922 under the title *A Theory of Natural Philosophy*. Bošković always wanted to visit Newton's homeland. Finally his wish became reality when he was sent on a mission to

London, and on 23 January 1760 he landed at Dover. The following day he went to Greenwich to see the famous observatory. In London he was well received in all circles, as his reputation amongst scientists and scholars had preceded him. He met Benjamin Franklin, who demonstrated to him his electrical experiments, and he dined with Dr Samuel Johnson. He also had discussions with representatives of the Church of England, and visited Oxford and Cambridge.

Bošković attended several meetings of the Royal Society in London, at which he stressed the importance of observing the imminent transit of Venus across the sun. He even submitted a Latin treatise to the Society entitled *De Proximo Veneris sub Sole Transitu*, which was published in volume 51 of *Philosophical Transactions* (1759-60). Soon afterwards, he dedicated to the Society his Latin poem *De solis et lunae defectibus* (*On the eclipses of the sun and the moon*), which was printed in London in the autumn of 1760. On 15 January 1761, the Royal Society elected Bošković a Fellow, a month after he had reluctantly left England (on 15 December 1760).

On leaving England, he travelled to Turkey. He returned to Italy in 1764, and became professor of mathematics at the University of Pavia, and director of the observatory at Brera. Sadly, his vanity, egotism and petulance made him many enemies, and in 1770 he removed to Milan. He was deprived of his post as a result of intrigues; and because of the suppression of the Jesuit order in 1773, he left Italy and accepted an invitation to Paris, where a post was arranged for him as director of optics for the navy. He remained in Paris for ten years, but his position became intolerable; therefore, in 1783, he returned to Italy and settled in Bassano. There he occupied himself with the publication of his five-volume *Opera pertinentia ad opticum et astronomicum* (Vienna, 1758). He then moved to Vallombrosa near Florence, and subsequently to Milan. There he fell into melancholia, lapsed into madness, and died on 3 February 1787 at the age of 75.

After Ruđer Bošković visited England, his theory of atomism spread throughout Great Britain and served as the basis for a number of scientific points of view during his lifetime. There is a long tradition in Britain relating to Bošković's theory of natural philosophy, set out in his seminal work *Theoria philosophiae naturalis* . . . (2nd ed., Venice, 1763). While he was still alive his theory was accepted by the famous British philosophical scientists Joseph Priestley and John Robinson. Although Bošković's theory and its application were discussed throughout Europe, there were differences between Great Britain and the rest of Europe. In Europe the theory was considered more critically, especially because of Bošković's belief that the fundamental particles of matter were immaterial atoms. It is certainly relevant that in Bošković's time the British were already trying to combine purely empirical facts with the philosophical tradition: this explains the subsequent attempts to reconcile Bošković's abstract natural philosophy with empiricism. Particularly important is Bošković's influence on five great men of British science: Humphry Davy, Michael Faraday, James Clerk Maxwell, Lord Kelvin and Joseph John Thomson.

Bošković's friend and compatriot Benedikt Stay-Stojković (1714-1801) from Dubrovnik was professor of rhetoric and history at the Collegio della Sapienza in Rome. He produced two large epic poems on natural philosophy in Latin. In the first: *Philosophiae versibus traditae libri VI* (Rome 1744) he expounded Descarte's philosophy in 10,249 Latin hexameters; in the second *Philosophiae recetionis* . . . *versibus traditiae libri X cum adnotationibus et supplementis R.J. Boscovich* (Rome I. 1755, II. 1760, III. 1792) helped by Bošković he explained Newton's natural philosophy and law of gravitation in 24,227 hexameters.

Among eighteenth-century chemists who wrote in Latin, one should mention Pavao Thaller (1735-1800), Josip Franjo Domin (1754-1819) and Ignjat Martinović (1755-1795).

Thaller, who lived and worked as a chemist in Požega (Slavonia), wrote a manual of chemistry entitled *Introductio ad Veram Chemiam* (1757) (241 pp. + 44 pp. addenda + 3 pp. of *Tabula affinitatis)*. This manuscript has never been published.

Franjo Domin studied philosophy, mathematics and physics at the Zagreb Academy, and obtained his diploma in 1776. In the same year he won a scholarship for postgraduate studies at the University of Trnava in Slovakia, where he obtained his PhD in 1777. Soon afterwards he was appointed Professor of Theoretical and Experimental Physics at the Academy of Györ in Hungary. There he lectured on Newton's laws, Bošković's atomic theory, and the kinetic theory of heat. In 1784, Domin published his first major work, *Dissertatio Physica . . .*, written in Latin. Translated into English, its full title is *Physical Treatise on the Genesis, Nature and Utility of Factitious Air*. It was the first work of this kind to be published in Hungary. "Factitious air" was an eighteenth-century term for any artificial gas differing from natural, atmospheric air. In this work Domin praises "the foremost modern physicists whose endeavour, under Priestley's leadership, raised this whole discipline to the level it now occupies".

Domin adhered to Priestley's theory of "phlogiston", which held that all combustible materials contain an element, phlogiston, which is given off when they burn. It was thought that when the air is saturated with phlogiston, it is less able to support combustion. Consequently, Priestley called the gas in which a candle flame burns brightly "dephlogisticated air". In fact, it is oxygen. When Domin wrote his *Physical Treatise*, the phlogiston theory was still generally accepted in the explanation of chemical phenomena. He used it conventionally, following Priestley's interpretation closely, although he was not a slavish adherent of the phlogiston theory. Domin was certainly one of the most competent experts in Priestleyan chemistry. However, in his *Physical Treatise*, he included the research and discoveries of other chemists apart from Priestley, such as J. Ingenhousz, T. Cavallo, F. Fontana, and others. He also paid considerable attention to the first aerostats, seeing in them a prospective application of the physics and chemistry of gases.

Ignjat Martinović, who taught natural sciences in Buda, Slavonski

33

Brod and Lviv (1783-91), was also a follower of the phlogiston doctrine. His manual of physical chemistry, *Prelectiones Physicae experimentalis I*, was published in Lviv (1787) and his mathematical work *Theoria generalis aequationum omnium graduum* in Buda (1780).

The 18th century botanist Augustin Michelazzi (1732-1820), a Jesuit from Rijeka, who taught physics and natural history at the lyceum in Gorica, is considered to be the first classifier of plants from Croatia. His comprehensive botanical manual entitled *Compendium Regni Vegetabilis* . . . [Goritiae, 1780] was of the same standard as its west European equivalents. "This was an important work, because it contained for that time contemporary notions on anatomy, systematization and physiology of plants"[5]

The 19th century botanists Visiani, Schlosser and Farkaš-Vukotinović continued to use Latin as the international language of botanical taxonomy and description.

Robert Visiani (1800-1878) from Šibenik produced an important work in Latin entitled *Flora Dalmatica* (Lipsiae, 1842-52, 3 vol.) and subsequently *Supplementa Florae Dalmaticae* (Venice, 1872 & 1882) in which the names of 27,000 different plants are recorded. This work provided valuable data to Josip Schlosser (1818-1882) and Ljudevit Farkaš-Vukotinović (1813-1893), the authors of *Flora Croatica* (Zagreb, 1869) in which 3,461 plant species are described. This was the last major Latin work printed in Croatia.

At the beginning of the 19th century, the mathematicians Paskvić and Wolfstein produced several works in Latin. Ivan Paskvić (1754-1829) from Senj studied at Graz and Buda. From 1786 he was both the astronomer at the Observatory of Buda (until 1824) and mathematics professor at the University of Buda (from 1788) and later in Vienna. He published several works in Latin and German in

---

[5] V. Grdinić, *An Illustrated History of Croatian Pharmacy*. Zagreb, Hrvatsko farmaceutsko društvo - Nakladni zavod Matice hrvatske, 1997. p.271.

the fields of astronomy, physics and mathematics.

Josip Wolfstein (1776-1859) from Karlovac studied at Pavia under the tutorage of Alessandro Volta and Lazaro Spallanzani. After completing his studies, he taught mathematics, first at Osijek (1797-1800), then at Košice (Slovakia) (1800-1820) and finally at the University of Pest (1820-1840), He wrote a few works on mathematics in Latin, such as *Introductio in theoriam motus* (Košice, 1800), *Elementa geometriae purae* (Košice, 1811) and *Introductio in mathesim puram* (1830-33, 3 vol.)

During the nineteenth century, when the social prestige of Latin began to decline, the direct relationship between Croatian and German or Hungarian gave rise to a new type of language question. During the Croatian national awakening, Ivan Derkos wrote, in a "neutral", supranational Latin, a book entitled *Genius patriae super dormientibus suis filiis* (*The Genius of Fatherland above His Sleeping Sons*, Zagreb, 1832), in which he appealed to all Croats to unite and to resist Germanisation and Magyarisation. He took Hugo Grotius's verses as the epigraph of his work:

> *O patriae salve lingua! Quam suam fecit*
> *Nec humilis unquam, nec superbi libertas . . .*
> *(Hail, language of our fatherland, your companion*
> *is freedom, never obsequious nor haughty . . .)*

Croats were the only people in the Roman Slavdom (*Slavia Romana*) who strongly resisted the Latin universalism of the Roman Church and tried to defend and assert their native language. As examples, witness the Croatian Glagolitic heritage; the Croat Protestant writers who in Urach, near Tübingen, printed books in the vernacular (1561-65); and the radically populist Bosnian Franciscans who in the seventeenth and eighteenth centuries, in their pastoral work and sermons, brought the Bible to the common people in their native tongue. Despite their success with the vernacular, these writers were constant in their belief that Latin was a more noble language. On the other hand, Latin provided access to western European culture, participation in the western *republica litterarum* and involvement in international affairs. As a relatively neutral, supranational lingua franca, Latin also served as a shield against Hungarian and German linguistic, political and cultural encroachments upon Croatia's body politic.

As a literary and cultural medium, Latin had been used in Croatia up to the mid-nineteenth century when it was superseded by literary Croatian. However, there were poets who wrote in Latin even in the twentieth century. Thus the poet and literary critic Ton Smerdel (1904-1970) published four collections of his Latin poems in the 1960s. It is worth noting that there are 4300 printed Latin works by Croatian authors up to 1848, as recorded in Šime Jurić's bibliography: *Opera scriptorum latinorum natione Croatorum usque ad annum MDCCCXLVIII typis edita, tom. I - Index alphabeticus, Zagrabiae 1968, tom. II - Index systematicus, Zagrabiae 1971.* In his *Bibliografia Hrvatska* (*Croatian Bibliography*, Zagreb, 1860), Ivan Kukuljević registered 3000 books written in Croatian up to 1860. Consequently, up to the mid-nineteenth century, Croatian authors had written more works in Latin than in Croat.

Works of Croatian Latinists

HERMANUS DALMATA - HERMAN DALMATIN
(fl. 1138-1143)

De Essentiis
Fourteenth-century manuscript.
Cotton Ms Titus D IV, ff. 75r - 138v

JOANNES DE RAGUSIO – IVAN STOJKOVIĆ (1390-1443)

Oratio, qua Joannes de Ragusio respondit per octo dies ad articulum primum Bohemorum de communione sub utraque specie. See CANISIUS (H.) Thesaurus Monumentorum, etc. tom. 4
1725. fol.
12.o.4

Johannis de Ragusio, Initium et prosecutio Basiliensis Concilii ... Nunc primum eruit Franciscus Palacky. See VIENNA. Oesterreichische Akademie der Wissenschaften. Monumenta conciliorum generalium seculi decimi quinti, etc. tom. 1.
1857, etc. 4°
5005.f.6

Johannis de Ragusio Tractatus quomodo Bohemi reducti sunt ad unitatem Ecclesiae ... Nunc primum erutus a Francisco Palacky. See VIENNA. Oesterreichische Akademie der Wissenschaften. Monumenta conciliorum generalium seculi decimi quinti, etc. tom. 1.
1857, etc. 4°
5005.f.6

[Three sermons] In: BRANDMUELLER (Walter) Das Konzil von Pavia-Siena, 1423-1424. Bd. 2. pp. 89-190.
1968, etc. 23cm. (Vorreformationsgeschichtliche Forschungen. Bd. 16).
Latin.
X.100/15009

VITEZ, JOANNES, Cardinal (1405-1472)

Epistolae in diversio negotiis statum publicum regni Hungariae concementibus, ab anno 1445 ad annum 1451, etc.
In: Schwandtnersus (J.G.) Scriptores Rerum Hungaricarum, etc. Tom. II.
1746, etc. fol.
149.g.2

J.V. Episcopi Varadiensis ... Orationes in cause expeditiones contra Turcas habitae, item Ae. Sylvii Epistolae ad eundem exaratae 1453-1457
Edidit Dr G. Fraknói. Budapestini, Vienna [printed] 1878. fol.
1856.b.3

SISGOREUS, GEORGIUS – JURAJ ŠIŽGORIĆ (1420-1509)

Elegije i pjesme (Elegie et Carmina)
U izboru preveo, uvod i bilješke napisao Nikola Šop, etc. [With illustrations]
Zagreb, JAZU, 1966. pp. 144. 8°. In: Hrvatski Latinisti, Knjiga 6
Ac.741/31(6)

CIPPICUS, CORIOLANUS – KORIOLAN ĆIPIKO (1425-1493)

Begin. [fol. 2 recto:] Coriolanus Cepio Clarissimo uiro Marco Antonio
Mauroceno ... felicitatem. [fol. 3 recto:] Coriolani Cepionis dalmatae Petri
Mocenici Imperatoris gestorum liber primus.
Per Bernardum Pictorem & Erhardum Ratdolt: Venetiis, 1477. 4°. 54 leaves,
the first and last blank.
IA.20488
[Another copy] On Vellum
C.5.a.36
[Another edition] Coriolani Ceponis ... De Patri Mocenici Imperatoris gestis
libri tres. Item Conradi Wengeri ... De bello inter Sigismundum
archistratagum Austriae & Venetos libellus. Praeterea Michaelis Coccinij ...
De Bellis italicis liber unus. [Edited by Joannes Heroldt.]
pp. 242. R. Winter: Basiliae, 1544. 8°
1440.a.15

[Another edition] Petri Mocenici, Imperatoris Veneti, gestorum contra Turcos libri III. See CHALCOCONDYLAS (L.) Laonici Chalcondylae ... De origine et rebus gestis Turcorum libri decem, etc.
1556. fol.
C.80.f.8
[Another edition] De bello Asiatico ... libri tres, opera Ioannis Cippici, nunc iterum impressi. ff.68.
Apud I.A. Ranpazettum: Venetiis, 1594. 8°
1194.a.26
[Another edition] Coriolani Cepionis ... De Petri Mecenici Venetae classis Imp. contra Ottomannum Turcarum principem rebus gestis. lib III. 1611. See JUSTINIANUS (P.) Rerum Venetarum ... historia, etc. Appendix 1610, etc. fol.
660.l.15.(2)

NICOLAUS, Bishop of Modrusch – NIKOLA MODRUŠKI (1427-1480)

Oratio in funere Reverendissimi domini. D. Petri Card. sancti Sixti habita a reverendo pre domino episcopo Nicolao modrusiensi
[1473?]. 4°. [Six leaves, without titlepage, pagination, or signatures; 30 lines to a full page.]
IA.18645
[Another edition] Begin. Oratio in funere ... Petri Cardinal' sancti Sixti habita a ... Nicolao episcopo modnisiensi [sic].
[Rome, 1474?]. 4°. [Ten leaves, without titlepage, pagination, or signatures; 30 lines to a full page.]
C.5.a.27
[Another edition] Begin. Oratio in funere ... domini Petri Cardinalis sancti Sixti, etc.
[Rome, 1477?] 4°. [Ten leaves, without titlepage, pagination, or signatures; 30 lines to a full page.]
IA.17814

Begin. [fol. 1. verso:] Oracio in funere Reuerendissimi domini dñi Petri Cardinalis, sancti sixti. Habita a renerendo [sic] pre domino Nicolao episcopo Modrusiensi

1475, etc. ff. 7 per matheum cerdonis: Padue, die penultima Augusti, 1482.
4°. [Eight leaves without titlepage or signatures. 32 lines to a page]
IA.29989

**PANNONIUS, IANUS, Bishop of Pécs – IVAN ČESMIČKI
(1434-1472)**

Pjesme i epigrami. Tekst i prijevod
Preveo Nikola Šop
Zagreb, 1951. p. XXII 354. 8°
In: Hrvatski Latinisti, Knjiga 2
Ac.741/31(2)

BENIGNUS, GEORGIUS – JURAJ DRAGIŠIĆ (1445-1520)

Homelia doctissima ... habita coram maximo Maximiliano Cesare, etc.
[Edited by G. Benignus][1508?] 4°
835.i.25.(2)

Disputatio nuper facta in domo magnifici Laurentii Medices [between N.
Mirabilis and G. Benignus on the proposition: "Peccatum Adae non est
maximum omnium peccatorum"]
1489. 4°
IA.27701

An Iudaeorum libri, quos Thalmud appellant ... Dialogus interlocutores
Ioannes Reuchlin, Georgius Benignus [By G. Benignus]
Luciani Piscator, etc. [1518] 4°
8461.c.26

Ad sanctissimum dominum nostrum Leonem papam decimum ... Apologia
... Iacobi hochstraten ... Contra dialogum G. Benigno ... in causa Ioannes
Reuchlin ascriptum, etc. [With the text of the dialogue]
1518. 4°
3910.bb.65

Begin. [fol. 1 recto:] Aelius Lampridius Cer. P.L. ad lectorem. [fol. 3 recto:]

Georgei Benigni ... in librum de natura caelestium spiritum quos angelos uocamus phemium incipit foeliciter. End. [fol. 130 recto:] Explicit opus de Natura Angelica, etc. [Bartolommeo di Libri:] Florentiae, xiii. Kalendas Augusti [20 July], 1499. fol.
IB.27385

Begin. [fol. 1 recto:] Georgii Benigni de Saluiatis ... ad optime indolis adolescentes ... magnanimi viri Laurentii Medicis filios in dialecticam nouam proemium incipit feoliciter [sic]. End. [fol. 94 verso:] Explicit foeliciter Dialectica noua secundum mentem Doctoris subtilis. Et beati Thome Aquinatis aliorum realista, etc.
Florentie, Die xviii mensis Martii, 1488. 8°
IA.27665

Propheticae Solutiones Georgii Benigni Ordinis Minorum.
p Laurentium de Morgianis: Florentiae, vi. idus April. [8 April], 1497. 4°
IA.27839

SIMON DALMATA PHARENSIS – ŠIMUN HVARANIN
(2nd half of the 15th century)

Begin. [fol. 1 verso:] Proemium. Et si multi sermonum scripturaque interpretationis, etc. [fol. 2 recto:] Opusculum presbyteri simonis dalmate ex ciuitate pharensi: in quo tractatur de baptismo sancti spiritus et virtute eius super euangelis Ioannis. Cap. 3.(e) Rat homo ex phariseis, etc.
Per Magistrum Guiliesmum [sic] gallum: uenetiis, die. xiiii. octobris, 1477. 4°. 44 leaves. Sig. a10 b-d8 e10. 27 lines to a page. Imperfect: wanting the first leaf.
IA.20713

PRIBOEVIUS, VINCENTIUS – VINKO PRIBOJEVIĆ
(Mid 15th – Mid 16th Century)

O podrijetlu i zgodama Slavena (De origine successibusque Slavorum)
Uvod i bilješke napisao i tekst za štampu priredio ... Grga Novak
Zagreb, JAZU, 1951. pp. 247. 8° In: Hrvatski Latinisti, Knjiga 1
Ac.741/31(1)

ZANE, BERNARDUS, Archbishop of Spalatro (c.1450-1527)

Begin. [fol. 3, preceded by the dedicatory epistle on two leaves:] Bernardi
Zane ... Oratio habita in prima Sessione Concili Lateraneñ. praesente Iulio
II. Pont. Opt. Max. [Edited by T. Niger]
Per Jacobum Mazocchium: Romae, 1512. 4°
IA.18396.(5.)

NIMIREUS, Archidiaconus Arbensis
MARTIN NIMIRA (2nd. half of the 15th century)

Begin. M. Nimireus Arbeñ Archidyaconus Reuerendissimo in Christo parti
et dño domino. B. tituli sanctorum Petri et Marcellini pro Cardinali
Carthagineñ dignissimo Salutem. [A sermon on Ps. xxii. 16, 17.]
[Rome, 1494.] 4°. Without titlepage, pagination or signatures. 10 leaves, 41
lines to a full page.
IA.18997

MARKO MARULIĆ (1450-1524)

M. Maruli Spalatensis bene vivendi instituta typo sanctorum salutariumque
doctrinarum congesta, etc. [Edited by D. Agricola]. ff. 279. cum Luca
Leonardo expensore, adamquae Petri de Langendorff Impressore: Basiliae,
1513. 4°
1412.f.30.(1)
[Another edition] M. Maruli opus de religiose vivendi institutione per
exempla ex veteri novoque testamente collecta; ex autoribus quoquae divo
Hieronymo presbytero, beato Gregorio Pont. Max., Eusebio Caesarieñ
episcopo, ... nonnullisque aliis qui vitas conscripsere sanctorum.
pp. 679. Apud sanctum Coloniam, 1531. 8°
848.b.9

M. Maruli Quinquaginta Parabole.
In edib. Petri Liechtenstein. Industria francisci lucensis: Venetiis, 1517. 8°
702.b.2

De humilitate et gloria Christi Maruli opus.
Bernardinus de Vitalib: Venetiis, 1519. 8°. After the colophon there follows
three pages of errata
4805.b.28

Euangelistarium Marci Maruli Spalatensis Viri disertissimi, opus uere
euangelicum ... in septem partitum libros. [With a preface by F. Julianius]
pp. 397. [Hoc preclarum opus administrat ... Joannes Koburger ... cuius
expensis ex officina ... Adae Petri ciuis Basiliensis emittitur, 1519.] 4°.
Imperfect; wanting the last leaf, with colophon. This copy was bound at
Cambridge, and contained in the cover fragments of an early edition of
Barclay's Eclogues.
C.64.d.13

Euangelistarium Marci Maruli ... opus vere Evangelicum cultissimoque
adornatum sermone: sub fidei; spei & charitatis titulus in septem partitum
libros. [Edited by Franciscus Lucensis. With a prefatory letter of Franciscus
Julianius.]
pp. 484. Apud Inclitam Coloniam, 1529. 8°. Imperfect; wanting pp. 15, 16.
843.k.12
[Another edition] pp. 639. Eucharius [Cervicornus] excudebat
Impensa & xre M. Godefrid Hittorpy. [Cologne,] 1529. 8°
843.k.13
[Another copy] Accessit Meginhardi ... ad ... Guntherum, de fide, varietate
symboli & ipso symbolo Apostolico ... libellus, etc. pp. 639. COPIOUS MS
NOTES.
Ex officina Eucharii Cervicor[ni, Cologne] 1529. 8°. A duplicate of the
preceding, with a new titlepage, preface and table of contents, and the
addition of the Libellus Meginhardi, which is without pagination.
843.k.14

Euangelistarium Marci Maruli Spalaten ... opus vere evangelicum, etc.
Apud Heronem Alopecium, aere & impensa Godefridi Hittorpij: Coloniae,
1532. 8°
4373.a.36

M. Maruli Spalatensis de vita religiose per exempla institvenda, etc. See
HEROLDT (J.) Basilius. Exempla virtutum et vitiorum, etc.

1555. fol.
612.l.9

[Another edition] M. Maruli Dictorum factorumque memorabilium libri sex; sive de bene beateque vivendi institutione ad normam vitae Sanctorum utriusque Testamenti, collecti atque in ordinem digesti, ... repurgati, ... per J. Foulerum, etc.
pp. 691. Apud J. Foulerum; typis Gerardi Smits, Antverpiae, 1577. 8°.
848.e.5

[Another edition] M. Maruli ... Dictorum factorumque memorabilium libri sex ... collecti atque in ordinem digesti, ... repurgati, ... per Ioan. Foulerum.
pp. 631. Apud Hieronymum de Marnef, & Viduam Gulielmi Cauellat; excudebat Petrus Hury: Parisiis, 1586. 8°. The date in the colophon: 1585.
4807.bbb.29

M. Maruli ... in eos, qui Beatum Hieronymum Italum esse contendunt. See LUCIO (G.) J. Lucii de Regno Dalmatiae et Croatiae libri sex, etc.
1666. fol.
149.f.4

See DALMATIA. Regvm Dalmatiae et Croatiae gesta. a M. Marulo ... Latinitate donata. (Commentariolum ... in Craina nuper repertum ... Dalmatico idiomate compositum.)
[J. Lucii De regno Dalmatiae, etc.]
1668. fol.
590.i.22

See DALMATIA. Regum Dalmatiae et Croatiae gesta. a M. Marulo ... latinitate donata.
1748. fol. [SCHWANDTNERUS (J.G.) Scriptores Rerum Hungaricarum, etc. tom. 3]
149.g.3

Ljetopis Popa Dukljanina. Uredio F. Šišić [the original Latin text with an early translation in Croatian, with a Latin translation of this version by M. Marulić]
1928. 8°
Ac.1131

44

Davidas. Priredio Josip Badalić. [The Latin text with an introduction in Croatian. With facsimiles.]
Zagreb, 1954. pp. 227. 8° [Stari pisci hrvatski. Knj. 3]
Ac.741/14

M. Maruli Davidiadis libri XIV. E codice Taurinensi in lucem protulit Miroslavus Marcovich, etc. [With facsimiles]
Mérida, 1957. pp. xxiv. 270. 8°. Publicaciones de la Dirección de Cultura de la Universidad de los Andes. no. 62.
11410.f.1

FELIX PETANTIUS (RAGUSINUS DALMATA) – FELIKS PETANČIĆ (1455-1517)

Quibus itineribus Turci sint aggrediendi. See KUR-AN [Latin]. Machumetis Sarracenorum principis vita, etc. tom. 3. [1543] fol.
696.i.10
tom. 3 1550. fol.
696.i.10
[Another edition] See HUNGARY [Appx.- Historical]. Rerum Hungaricarum Scriptores varii, etc. 1600. fol.
C.77.g.5
[Another edition] See CORINGIUS (H) De Bello contra Turcas prudenter gerendo libri varii. 1664. 4°
835.e.3.(5)
[Another edition] See SCHWANDTNERUS (J.G.) Scriptores Rerum Hungaricarum, etc. tom. 1 1746, etc. fol.
149.g.1

CERVARIUS TUBERO (LUDOVICUS) – LUDOVIK CRIJEVIĆ TUBERON (1459-1527)

Ludouici Ceruarii Tuberonis ... De Turcarum origine, moribus, & rebus gestis commentarius. [Edited by F. Serdonati]
pp. 129. Apud. A. Patauinium: Florentiae, 1590. 4°
10125.bb.18

Ludouici Tuberonis ... Commentatorium de rebus, quae temporibus eius in illa Europae parte, quam Pannonii & Turcae eorumq; finitimi incolunt, gestae sunt, libri videcim.
[Edited by M. Adelarius] pp. 354. Impensis C. Marnij, & haeredum I. Aubrij: Francofurti, 1603. 4°
C.76.c.18
[Another copy]
C.73.c.7.(2)
[Another edition] Ludouici Tuberonis ... Commentatiorum de rebus, suo tempore, nimirum ab anno Christi MCCCCXC. vsque ad annum Christi MDXXII. in Pannonia, et finitimis regionibus gestis libri XI. ... Recogniti, emendati, et synopsibus aucti. 1746. See SCHWANDTNER (J.G. von) Scriptores rerum Hungaricarum, etc. tom. 2
1746, etc. fol.
149.g.2

Commentariolus L. Cervarii Tuberonis de origine et incremento urbis Rhacusanae, ejusdemque ditionis descriptio, auctore Nicolao Joannis de Bona, et Stephani Gradi Antiquitatum Rhacusanarum diatriba. His accedit de illustribus familiis, quae Rhacusae extant ... elegia Didaci Pyrrhi. Cum notis et supplementis.
[Edited by M. de Sorgo] pp. 83. Rhacussi, 1790. 4°
665.d.3

BENJA, ŠIMUN, called KOŽIČIĆ, Bishop of Modruš (1460-1536)

See VIGERIUS (M.) Cardinal. Controversia de excellentia instrumentorum Dominicae Passionis, etc. [Edited by Š. Benja, Bishop of Modrusch.]
1512. 4°
C.42.c.6.

Simo Begnii ... Oratio in sexta Lateran̄. Concilii sessione. Quinto Kalen̄. Maias habita. M.D.XIII
[1513?] 4°
834.e.1.(14)
[Another copy] [Simo Begnii ... Oratio in sexta Lateran̄. Concilii sessione.]
[Rome, 1513.] 4°. Imperfect; wanting the title-leaf.
1489.t.67

BONUS, IACOBUS – JAKOV BUNIĆ (1469-1534)

Begin. [fol. 1 verso: Reverendissimo in Christo patri D. Oliverio Carraphae Cardinali Napolitano episcopo Sabinen. protectori Ragusino Iacobus Bonus] [fol. 2 recto:] Iacobi Boni Epidaurii Dalmatae de raptu Cerberi Liber Primus. [In verse.]
[Stephan Plannck: Rome, 1490?] 4°
IA.18487
[Another edition] Iacobi Boni ... De raptu Cerberi libri tres. See OVIDIUS NASO (P.) [Metamorphoses – Latin] P. Ovidii Nasonis Metamorphoseon libri XV, etc. 1538. 8°
11405.aaa.45.(2)

IACOBI BONI ... De vita et gestis Christi eiusquae mysteriis & documentis opus egregium ... carmine heroico eleganter ac mirifice congestum ... Eiusdem Iacobi Praeludium in treis distinctum libros, trium gratiarum nominibus appellatos, atque Herculis labores & gesta in Christi figuram, mystice ac pulcherrime eodem carmine continentes. pp. ccxcviii. [F.M. Calvo?] Romae, 1526. fol.
11408.h.12

BRODERICUS, STEPHANUS – STJEPAN BRODARIĆ, (1471-1539), Successively Bishop of Sirmium and of Waitzen

Clades in campo Mohacz, in qua Ludouicus occidit, a D. Stephano Broderith ... descripta. See BONFINIUS (A) Antonii Bonfinii Rerum Ungaricarum decades quatuor, etc.
1568. fol.
590.l.12
[Another edition] See SCHARDIUS (S.) Historicum opus, etc. tom. 2. [1574.] fol.
9366.i.11
[Another edition] See BONFINIUS (A) Antonii Bonfinii Rerum Ungaricarum decades quatuor, etc.
1581. fol.
9315.k.8

[Another edition] See REUSNER (N.) Rerum memorabilium in Pannonia ... gestarum exegeses, etc.
1603. 4°
C.73.c.7.(1)
[Another edition] See SCHARDIUS (S.) Schardius redivivus, etc. tom. 2
1673. fol.
9366.l.6
[Another edition] Clades Mohaciensis Broderithii (recognita à Sambuco).
See BONFINIUS (A.) Antonii Bonfinii Historia Pannonica, etc.
1690. fol.
149.f.13
[Another edition] Stephani Broderici ... Cladis Mohacsianae sub Ludovico II. descriptio a Joanne Sambuco olim recognita. [1755?] See EPHEMERIDES. Calendarium Jaurinense, etc.
1756. [1755, etc.] 8°
P.P.2441.b.
[Another edition] De clade in campo Mohacz ... anno M.D.XXVI. narratio. See REUSNER (N.) Rerum memorabilium in Pannonia ... gestarum narrationes, etc.
1770. 4°
9315.ee.13

POLICARPUS, JOANNES SEVERITANUS (1472-1526)

See DONATUS (A.) [Ars minor.] Dionisii: appollonii donati: de octo orationis partibus libri ... cum comentarijs. M. Io. Policarpi, etc.
1517. 4°
1560/1821

FRANGIPANIBUS CHRISTOPHOROS DE, Count (1482-1527)

Oratio ad Adrianum Sextum, Pont. Max. C. de Frangepanibus [on aggressions by the King of Croatia. – Memoriale ... ad Papam, against the Turks, etc.]
[Paris, 1523?]
835.f.32.

FRANGEPANIBUS WOLFGANGUS DE, Count of Tersath –
VUK FRANKAPAN (+ 1546)

Oratio ad ... Carolum v, ... ac ad ... principes Romani imperii, facta, ex parte regnicolarum Croaciae, ... 24 Aug. 1530 habita, Responsio ... Joachini Marchionis Brandenburgensis, etc. [Edited by C. Churrerius] Augustae Vindelicorum, 1530. 4°
1315.b.69.(2.)

FRANGEPAN, FRAN – FRAN FRANKAPAN (+ 1543)

Oratio ad Caesarem, Electores et principes Germaniae, (habita Ratisponae IX Junij, anno 1541) Augustae Vindelicorum, 1541. 4°
1315.c.4.(4.)

See BESSARION (J.) cardinal, etc. Orationes duae accuratissimae ... Ex officina typographica I. Hofmanni: Noribergae, 1593. 8°
1053.b.37

ANDRONICUS TRANQUILLUS PARTHENIUS –
ANDREIS FRAN TRANKVIL (1490-1571)

Tranquil Andronici Dalmatae ad optimates Polonos admonitio Few MS Notes.
H. Viet[or]: Cracouiae, 1545. 4°
8094.aa.18
[Another edition] Cum praefatione Iacobi Gorscii, etc. In: officina Lazari. Cracouiae, 1584. pp. 53. 4°
8092.b.8

Oratio de laudibus eloquentiae ... in Gymnasio Lipsensi pronunciata. Ex officina M. Lottheri: Lipsiae, 1518. 4°
012301.ee.1

PASCHALIS, LUDOVICO – LUDOVIK PASKALIĆ, (c. 1500-1551)

L. Pascalis, J. Camilli, Molsae, et aliorum illustrium poetarum carmina, ... per L. Dulcium nunc primum in luce aedita.
Venetiis, 1551. 8°
11408.aa.3
[Another copy]
11409.aa.44.(6.)

Carmina. See ITALIAN POETS. Carmina illustrium Poetarum Italorum. tom. 7.
1719, etc. 8°
657.a.22

GARBITIUS MATTHIAS – MATIJA GRBIĆ (GRBAC) (1503/8-1559)

Aeschyli Prometheus. Cum interpretatione M. Garbitii. Greek and Latin.
1559. 8°
998.a.27
1767. 8°
822.e.1

Aristae De legis divinae ... translatione, etc. Greek and Latin. See ARISTEAS, Officer of the Court of Ptolemy Philadelphus
[1561]. 8°
1004.b.15

Hesiodi Opera et Dies: annotationes ... G. debentur. See CRESPIN (J.) Ta soksomena ton palaiotaton poieton georgica, etc. [In Greek.]
Vetustissimorum authorum georgica, etc. Greek and Latin.
[1570, etc.] 16°
1067.b.1
1600. 16°
996.a.5
1629. 16°
1067.b.2

1639. 16°
1067.b.3

See GIANI (A.) Annalium sacri ordinis Fratrum Servorum B. Maria Virginis
... Centuriae quatuor ... Editio secunda, cum notis ... opera ... F.A.M. Garbij.
(Sacri Annales ... ab anno 1609 [-1705] auctore ... A.M.Garbio)
1719, etc. fol.
4783.h.1

Aristae, de legis divinae ex Hebraica lingua in Graecam translatione, per
septuaginta interpretes facta, historia, M.G. interprete. Greek and Latin. See
JOSEPHUS (F.)
F. Josephi ... Opera omnia Graece et Latine, etc. tom. 2. (App.)
1726. fol.
681.i.2

VERANCIUS ANTONIUS – ANTUN VRANČIĆ (1504-1573)

Iter Buda Hadrianopolim. See FORTIS (A.) Viaggio in Dalmazia, etc. vol.
1
1774. 4°
454.a.13

Iter Buda Hadrianopolim anno 1553 exaratum ab. A. V., ... nuno primum ...
in lucem editum [by A. Fortis]. Venetiis, 1774. 4°
664.c.23

Iter Buda Hadrianopolim. See FORTIS (A.) Travels into Dalmatia, etc.
1778. 4°
149.d.3

De rebus gestis Joannis Regis Hungariae libri II. ... Fragmentum. -De situ
Transylvaniae, Moldaviae, et Transalpinae, fragmentum. -Castigationes ...
in Jovium: fragmentum. -De itinere et legatione sua Constantinopolitana
A.V. cum fratre suo Michaele dialogus: fragmentum. -Summa successus
ultimae actionis Legatorum A.V., F. Zay, et A. a Busbecche apud Principem
Turcarum Zoleimanum habitae 1557 mense Augusto. See KOVACHICH
(M.G.) Scriptores rerum Hungaricarum minores, etc. tom. 2.

51

1798. 8°
1438.e.9

Joannis Regis Hung. decessus ... A.C. 1540 perscriptus. See KOVACHICH
(M.G.) Scriptores rerum Hungaricarum minores, etc. tom. 1.
1798. 8°
1438.e.9

BARTHOLOMAEUS [GEORGIEUITS] – BARTOL
GEORGIJEVIĆ (c. 1506-1566)

De afflictione tam captiuorum quàm etiam sub Turcae tributo viuentium
Christianorum ... additis nonnullis vocabulis, Dominica oratione, Angelica
salutatione, symbolo Apostolorum linguae Sclauonicae, cum interpretatione
Latina, libellus. Autore Bartholomaeo Georgij, etc.
Typis Copenij: Anuerp., 1544. 8°
C.32.a.6.(1)
[Another issue] Typis Copenij: Anuerp., 1544. 8°
G.7297.(2)

De Turcarum ritu et caeremoniis ... Additis quam plurimis dictionibus, etiam
numero, cum salutationibus & responsionibus Persarum.
Apud Gregorium Bontium: Antuerpiae, 1544. 8°. Bound up for the Emperor
Charles V. with the Exhortatio contra Turcas.
C.46.b.21.(1)
[Another copy.]
G.7297.(1)

Epistola exhortatoria contra infideles, ad Illustrissimum Principem
Maximilianum Archiducem Austriae, Bartholomaei Georgieuits. See
MOHAMMEDANS. Prognma, siue praesagium Mehemetanorum, etc.
[1545.] 4°
1197.d.13.(7)

Exhortatio contra Turcas. Ad Illustrissimum Principem Maximilianum
Archiducem Austriae ... Bartholomaeus Georgieuits clientum humillimus.
Antuerpiae, 1545. 8°. Bound for the Emperor Charles V.
C.46.b.21.(2)

Prognoma, siue praesagium Mehemetanorum ... ex Persica lingua [or ratherm from the Turkish] in Latinum sermonem conuersum. Auth. Bartholomaeo Georgieuits. See MOHAMMEDANS.
[1545.] 4°
1197.d.13.(7)

Haec noua, fert Affrica. Mysterium sanctissimae Trinitatis. Arabicé ... Pro Fide Christiana cum Turca disputationis habitae, & mysterio sanctiss. Trinitatis in Alchorano inuento, nunc primum in latinum sermonem uerso, breuis descriptio. Authore Barptholomaeo Georgieuits. (Iis addita sunt nonnulla lectu digna ... dominica oratio, Angelica salutatio, Symbolum Apostolorum, ex Latino in Turcicum sermonem versa. -Incipit procnoma Turcicum de Christianorum calamitatibus, deinde de suae gentis interitu. - Exortatio contra Turcas)
Haeredes Syngrenii, cura et expensis Barptholomaei Georgieuits: Viennae, 1548. 8°
4506.a.22

Epistola exhortatia contra infideles, ad Illustrissimum Principem Maximilianum Archiducem Austriae, Bartholomaei Georgieuits. -De afflictione, tam captiuorum quàm etiam sub Turcae tributo uiuentium Christianorum: similiter de ritu, decquae ceremonijs domi, militiaequae ab ea gente usurpatis: additis nonnullis lectu dignis, linguarum Sclauonicae & Turcicae, cum interpretatione Latina, libellus, etc. See KUR'AN. [Latin] Machumetis Saracenorum principis, eiusque successorum uitae, etc. tom. 3 1550. fol.
696.l.10

Machumetis Saracenorum principis, eiusque successorum vitae, etc. tom. 3. 1550. fol. [KUR'AN. [Latin]]
696.l.10

Libellus uere Christiana lectione dignus diuersas res Turcharum breui tradens. Barpt. Geor. p.h. authore. [Containing the two works "De aflictione captivorum, etc." and "De Turcarum ritu et caeremoniis", with additions.]
Impressum apud A. Bladum; Venditur ... apud Magistrum Ioannem: Romae. 1552. 8°
G.7298

De Turcarum Moribus epitome, Bartholomaeo Georgieuiz Peregrino Autore. (De Turcarum ritu et caeremoniis capitulum, etc. -De afflictione ... Christianorum. -Exhortatio contra Turcas. [With the Vaticinium and various dialogues and versions of the Lord's prayer, Ave Maria, etc.])
pp. 184. Apud Ioan. Tornaesium: Lugduni, 1553. 16°
10126.a.38

De Turcarum Moribus epitome. See TURKS. De origine Imperii Turcorum eorumque administratione & disciplina, etc.
1562. 8°
280.b.17
[Another edition] De Turcarum Moribus epitome.
pp. 184. Apud Ioan. Tornaesium: Lugduni, 1578. 16°
803.a.15

De Turcarum Moribus epitome, Bartholomaeo Georgieuiz Peregrino Autore.
pp. 184. Apud Ioan. Tornaesium: Lugduni, 1568. 16°
569.a.31

De Turcarum caeremoniis religione, natura & moribus. Item de Christianorum debellatorum atquae captiuorum conflictione. (Disputatio alia iucunda habita cum Turca à Bartholomaeo Georgieuiz Peregrino. - Vaticinium infidelium lingua Turcica.) See GEUFFROY (A.) Aulae Turcicae. Othomannicique imperii descriptio, etc.. pt. 1
1577. 8°
9135.aa.1

Liber tertius de Rebus Turcicis, ex Bartholomaei Georgieuiz ... Epitome desumptus. See LONICERUS (P.) Chronicorum Turcicorum ... tomus primus [etc.] tom. 1.
1578. fol.
434.i.17
[Another edition] See LONICERUS (P.) Chronicorum Turcicorum ... tomus primus [etc.] tom. 1.
1584. 8°
1053.a.3

Bartholomaei Georgieuiz Exhortatio contra Turcas, ad Maximilianum II. Bohemiae Regem. 1596. See REUSNER (N.) Selectissimarum orationum

et consultationum de bello Turcico ... centuriae quatuor, etc. vol 1.
1596, etc. 4°
75.a.17

De Turcarum Moribus epitome. (De Turcarum ritu et ceremoniis. [With a
dialogue and a version of the Lord's prayer.]) See GISLENIUS (A.)
Seigneur de Busbecq. Aug. Gislenii Busbequii quae extant omnia, etc.
1660. 12°
1084.a.17

De Turcarum Moribus epitome.
pp. 184. Apud Ioan. de Tournes: [Lyons] 1629. 16°
10125.a.43
[Another edition] De Turcarum Moribus libellus in quo de eorum templis,
quadragesima, circumcisione ... militia, oeconomia & aliis pluribus lectu
jucundis agitur. Bartholomaeo Georgieuiz Peregrino auctore.
pp. 80. Typis & sumptibus Johannis Heilmulleri: Helmestadii, 1671. 4°
1197.d.13.(6)

**BONA DE BOLICIS, IOANNES – IVAN BONA
BOLICA (1520-1570)**

Descriptio Ascriuensis vrbis. [In verse]. See RAZZI (S.) La storia di Raugia,
etc.
[1595.] 4°. [Description of the city of Kotor]
795.f.19.(1)

FLACIUS, MATTHIAS ILLYRICUS (1520-1575)

Apologia Matthiae Flacii Illyrici ad Scholam Vitebergensem in Adiaphorum
causa. Eiusdem Epistola de eadem materia ad Philip. Melantho. Item
quaelam alia eiusdem generis.
Per Michaelem Lottherum: Magdeburgi, 1549. 8°. 48 leaves without
pagination.
3906.a.68.(1.)

Clarissimae quaedam notae uerae ac falsae religionis atque adeo ipsius Antichristi; ex quibus etiam rudiores ... statuere queant doctrinam nostram esse ueram ... Papistarum uero falsam, etc.
Michael Lotther: Magdeburgi, 1549. 8°
3908.de.10

Confutatio Catechismi larvati Sydonis Episcopi [M. Helding, etc.] FEW MS. NOTES
[Magdeburg?] 1549. 8°
3908.a.10

See GAL: (NIC:) and ILLY: (MATTH: FLA:) Contio poenitentiae proposita publicis peccatoribus hujus temporis in instaurata Ecclesia ... Per Nic[olaum] Gal[lum] et Matth[iam] Fla[cium] Illy[ricum], etc.
[1549?] 8°
698.a.42.(8.)

Declaratio turpitudinis peccati eorum qui per concilium, Interim aut Adiaphora a Christo ad Antichristum deficiunt, etc. [with woodcuts.]
Apud Christianum Rhodium: Magdeburgi, [c. 1549] 4°
1473.c.46

De vocabulo fidei et aliis quibusdam vocabulis, explicatio uera & utilis; sumta ex fontibus Ebraicis ... Cum praefatione Phil. Mel.
Apud Vitum Creucer: Vitebergae, 1549. pp. 188.
3908.de.11

Epistola apologetica M. Flacii ad quendam pastorem. Item duo somnia Philippi [Melancthonis; relative to the Adiaphoristic controversy]
[Magdeburg? 1549?] 8°
698.a.42.(5.)

Quod hoc tempore nulla penitus mutatio in religione sit in gratiam impiorum facienda. Contra quoddam scriptum incerti autoris, in quo suadetur mutatio piarum caeremoniarum in Papisticas. Per Hermanum Primatem.
[Magdeburg?] 1549. 8°. With the arms of the Marquis de Morante stamped in gold on the covers.
3906.a.47

Quod locus Lucae VII. Dico tibi remissa sunt ei peccata multa, nam dilexit multum, nihil Pharisaicae justiciae patrocinetur.
Magadaburgi, 1549. 8°. Seven leaves, without pagination. With the arms of the Marquis de Morante stamped in gold on the covers.
3906.a.50

Responsio Matthiae Flacij Illyrici ad epistolam Philippi Melanthonis
Magdeburgae, 1549. 8°
3908.de.9

Amica humilis et devota admonitio M[atthiae] F[lacii] Illyr[ici] ad gentem sanctam ... de corrigendo sacrosancto canone deissae. See ILLYR. (M.F.)
Amica ... admonitio, etc.
1550. 8°
3902.aa.26

See CLERGY. Cleri Fletus, etc. [With a preface by M.F.]
1550. 12°
11409.b.14

Duo scripta duorum doctorum ... virorum Lipsiae adiaphoricis corruptelis opposita ... Item epistolae aliquot ejusdem argumenti, etc. [Edited with a preface by M.F.]
Magdeburgae, 1550. 8°
3906.a.51

Omnia Latina scripta Matthiae Flacii Illyrici, hactenus sparsim contra Adiaphoricas fraudes et errores aedita, et quaedam prius non excusa, etc.
Magdeburgae, 1550. 8°
847.h.4.

Responsio M.F[lacii] Illyrici ad maledicta D.G. Maioris, maximi Christi & Belial ... conciliatoris, & nuovum Interim propugnatoris.
[1550?] 8°. See F., M., Illyricus.
3908.de.9

Scriptum contra primatum Papae, ante annos 100 compositum. Item Matthiae Flacij Illyrici de eadem materia.

Apud Christianum Rhodium: Magdeburgi, [1550.] 8°
3908.de.13

See TRENT, Council of. Recusatio Tridentinae Synodi ... 1546 a statibus
Augustanae Confessionis ... Rationes, item, [By M.F.] ... cur ejusmodi
Synodi etiamnum devitandae sint.
[1550?] 8°
1020.K.K.I.(1.)

De Iesu, nomine Christi seruatoris nostri proprio, contra Osiandrum. De
Iehoua nomine ueri Dei proprio.
Ex officina Iohannis Cratonis: Wittebergae, 1552. 4°
1473.c.45

Pia quaedam vetustissimaque poemata, partim Antichristum ejusque
spirituales filiolos insectantia, partim etiam Christum, ejusque beneficium
mira spiritus alacritate celebrantia. [By Hildebertus?] Cum praefatione Math.
Flacii Illyrici.
Magdeburgae, 1552. 16°
11405.b.13

De Voce et Re Fidei, contra pharasaicum hypocritarum fermentum ... Cum
praefatione P. Melancthonis
Basiliae, [1554.] 8°
3908.bb.37

Historia certaminum inter Romanos Episcopos & sextam Carthaginensem
synodum Africanasque Ecclesias, de primatu seu potestate Papae, etc.
Basiliae, [1554?] pp. 214. 8°
4534.a.10

Catalogus testium veritatis, qui ante nostram aetatem reclamarunt Papae.
Cum praefatione M. Flacii Illyrici.
Per J. Oporinum: Basiliae, 1556. 8°. The titlepage is slightly mutilated.
847.g.7
[Another edition] See FL. (M.) Illyricus. Catalogus, etc.
1608. fol.
C.82.k.2
[Another edition] Accurata nunc recensione ... additis nonnullis notis ... una

58

cum auctoris opusculorum ac testimoniorum, qua editorum, qua ineditorum, eoque seorsim editis [by J.C. Dieterich]. (M.F. Tres aurei tractatus I. De synodo VI. carthaginensi. II. De Petri primatu. III. De electione episcoporum.) 3 pt.
Francofurti, Cattopoli, 1666-67. 4°. Pt. 2 and 3 have each a separate pagination and titlepage, with the imprint Cattopoli, 1667.
4886.f.13.
[Another copy] 3 pt.
Francofurti, Cattopoli, 1672-67. 4°
Pt. 1 and 2 are duplicates of the corresponding pt. in the edition of Frankfort, 1666 ... with a new titlepage and dedicatory epistle to pt. 1; pt. 3 is a reprint.
119.b.2.
[Another copy]
Francofurti, Gissae, Cattopoli, 1672-67. 4°. The titlepage of pt. 2 is reprinted, and bears the imprint Gissae, 1672.
1371.g.21.(1.)

Varia doctorum piorumque virorum de corrupto Ecclesiae statu poemata, ante nostram aetatem conscripta ... Cum praefatione Mathiae Flacii Illyrici.
Per Ludovicum Lucium: Basiliae, 1557. pp. 494. 8°
11409.ccc.23
[Another copy] Varia doctorum piorumque virorum de corrupto Ecclesiae statu poemata, etc. MS. NOTES.
[Basiliae, 1557.] 8°. Wanting the last leaf, bearing the imprint.
238.m.29
[Another copy]
G.17463

See WERNERUS (T.) Epistola ... scripta ex mandato F. Illyrici & praescripta ab eo formula ... in qua quid sentiat F. *Peri Logou* ...exponitur, etc.
1558. 4°
3906.c.97.(6.)

See ROME, *Church* of. PAUL III., Pope. Scripta quaedam Papae et Monarcharum ... cum prefatione M.F. Illyrici.
[1560?] 8°
C.36.d.23.(4.)

See ROME, *Church* of. PIUS IV., Pope. Indulgentia plenaria pro pace conservanda, etc. [With a prefatory note by M.F.]
[1560?] 4°
4061.e.41

Ecclesiastica Historia, integram Ecclesiae Christi ideam quantum ad locum, propagationem, persecutionem tranquillitatem, doctrinam, haereses, ceremonias, gubernationem, schismata, synodos, personas, miracula, martyria, religiones extra Ecclesiam, et statum Imperii politicum attinet, secundum singulas centurias ... complectens ... Per aliquot studiosos et pios viros in urbe Magdeburgicae, [viz. M.F., J. Wigandus, M. Judex, B. Faber, A. Corvinus, and T. Holthuter.] Accessit ... rerum in singulis centuriis ... Index. 13 cent.
Basiliae, 1562-74. fol. The colophon of Cent 4 is dated 1561.
C.81.i.39????
[Another edition] Ecclesiastica Historia, etc. Basiliae, 1564, 61-74. fol.
699.m.1-7
[Another edition] Historiae Ecclesiasticae volumen primum, etc. 1624. fol.
4534.i.1
[Another edition] Centuriae Magdeburgenses, seu historia eclesiastica Novi Testamenti, cum variorum theologorum continuationibus ad haec nostra tempora, quas excipient supplementa emendationum, defensionum, illustrationumque ad priores centurias XIII. Quorum curam suscipiet, qui praefationes etiam singulis voluminibus addet, S.J. Baumgarten [and J.S. Semler. Edited by J.J. Hauckius] 4 vol.
Norimbergae, 1757, 58, 60, 65. 4°
D.3224.e.13
[Another copy of vol. 1,2.]
210.a.1

Disputatio de originali peccato et libero arbitrio, inter M. Flacium Illyricum et V. Strigelium publice vinariae, anno 1560 ... habita ... Accesserunt ejusdem argumenti et alia quaedam scripta, ejusdem disputationis occasione, etc. [Edited by S. Musaeus] MS. NOTES.
[Bremen?] 1562. 4°
4256.b.13

Catalogus testium ueritatis, qui ante nostram aetatem Pontifici Romano, eiusque erroribus reclamarunt: iam denuò longè quam antea, & emendatior

& auctior editus ... Cum Praefatione Mathiae Flacii Illyrici, etc.
Argentinae; ex officina Ioannis Oporini: Basiliae, 1562. pp. 568. 58. fol.
1486.g.6

Fidelis Admonitio de Sacrosancto Jesu Christi Testamento incorrupto ac in
suo nativo sensu, contra omnes imposturas et Sophismata hominum.
Ratisponae, 1562. 4°
3906.aaa.81

De translatione Imperii Romani ad Germanos. Item de electione
episcoporum, quod aeque ad plebem pertineat. Accessit ejusdem argumenti
liber Lupoldi Babembergensis de juribus imperii & regni Rom. (Cum aliis
nonnullis libellis. Ludovici IIII. imperatoris contra Joannis XXII. bullam
responsio, concernens jura regni & imperii. -Donationis quae Constantini
dicitur ... privilegium, B. Picerno de monte arduo, interprete. -U. Hutteni in
libellum L. Vallae contra effictam & ementitam Constantini donationem. -
Laurentii Valensis de ... ementita Constantini donatione declamatio. [Edited
by B.J. Herold])
Basiliae, 1566. 8°. 2 vol.
1054.b.1.(1-2)
[Another edition] Francofurti, DCXII. [1612.] 4°
1054.h.8

M. Flacii ... Refutatio Sophismatum et elusionum, quae pro sacramentorio
errore contra sacro-sanctum Testamentum Christi afferri solent, etc.
[Basle?] 1657. 8°
3906.aa.49

Epistola de morte Pauli Tertii Pontificis Max. [By Publius Aesquillos, i.e. M.
Flacius.] In: ROSARIUS (Simon) pp. 129-147
Antithesis Christi et Antichristi, etc. 1578. 8°.
1413.d.5

See LUTHER (M.) [Selections, etc.] De locorum theologicorum ... P.
Melanthonis orthodoxa puritate ... adsertio ... Martini Lutheri, M.F. Illyrici,
etc.
1579. 4°
3906.c.97.(8.)

61

Catalogus testium veritatis, qui ante nostram aetatem Pontifici Romano atque Papismi erroribus reclamarunt. Postrema hac editione emendatior & dupló auctior redditus, etc. (Catalogi testium veritatis ... tomus secundus ... S.G.S. [i.e. Simon Goulart] studio, vt & tomus prior ... auctior redditas, etc.) 2 tom.
Ex typographia A. Candidi: Lugdun., 1597. 4°
850.l.2.

Clauis Scripturae ... Editio vltima. 2 pt.
Per Sebastianum Henricpetri: Basiliae, 1617. fol.
1492.h.13

Clavis Scripturae Sacrae, seu de Sermone sacrarum literarum, in duas partes divisae ... Editio nova, etc. [Edited by C. Grubelius.] 2 pt.
Impensis Johannis Ludovici Neuenhahns: Jenae, 1674. fol. The titlepage of pt. 2 bears the words: "Editio ultima"
3914.h.8.

Clavis Scripturae Sacrae, seu de sermone sacrarum literarum, in duas partes divisae ... Editio nova auctior ex recensione T. Suiceri. (Refutatio libri de peccato originis; ... Authore J. Musaeo.) 2 pt.
Lipsae, 1695. fol. There is also a second titlepage engraved, the imprint of which is Hafniae, 1695.
L.6.e.4
[Another copy] Clavis Scripturae Sacrae, etc.
3105.c.3

See BACMEISTER (J.) Acta Philippica. Sive: theologorum Saxonicorum & legatorum Megapolensium frustra tentata pacificatio inter Philippum Melanchthonem & Matthiam Flacium, etc.
1719. 4°
3905.bbb.104

De ratione cognoscendi Sacras literas. Über den Erekenntnisgrund der Heiligen Schrift. Lateinisch-deutsche Parallelausgabe übersetzt eingleitet und mit Anmerkungen versehen von Lutz Geldsetzer. (Photomechanischer Nachdruck des lateinischen Textes aus der letzten Ausgabe der Clavis Scripturae Sacrae von Johannes Musaeus, Frankfurt und Leipzig 1719.) Düsseldorf: Stern-Verlag Janssen & Co., [1968] pp. 112; port. 21cm.

(Instrumenta philosophica. Series hermeneutica. no. 3.)
X.208/1494

Editio nova auctior ex recensione T. Suiceri. (Accessit sub calcem refutatio libri de peccato originis, huic parti ab authore inserti; et admonitio brevis de locis nonnullis in parte utraque, quod cautum lectorem desiderent ... authore J. Musaeo) 2 pt. MS. NOTES
Francofurti et Lipsiae, 1719. fol.
691.i.12,13

See COLERUS (J.) Historia disputationis ... inter Jac: Colerum et Math: Flacium Illyricum, de peccato originis, etc.
1726. 8°
3902.a.1

See COLER (J.) Colloquium de peccato originis inter J. Colerum et M.F., etc.
1740. 8°
4378.aa.54.(3.)

Varia doctorum piorumque virorum de corrupto Ecclesiae statu poemata ... nunc altera vice ob insignem libelli raritatem publicae luci exposita [Frankfort on the Main] 1754. 8°. pp. 500
1213.k.29

Cataloguis testium veritatis [with a portrait]
Zagreb, JAZU, 1960. pp. LXXIII 341. 8°. In: Hrvatski Latinisti, Knjiga 5
Ac.741/31(5)

PATRIZI, FRANCESCO – FRANJO PETRIĆ (1529-1597)

F. Patricii de legendae scribendaequae [sic] Historiae ratione Dialogi decem, ex Italico in Latinum sermonem conversi. J.N. Stupano ... interprete.
Basiliae, 1570. 8°.
580.a.4
[Another edition] F. Patritii de historia dialogi x. ... J.N. Stupano ... interprete. See BODIN (J.) Political writer. J. Bodini Methodus historica, etc.

1576. 8°
580.c.9
[Another edition] See WOLFIUS (JOANNES) Jurist. Artis historicae penus, etc. tom. 1.
1579. 8°
304.a.5

F. Patritii Discussionum Peripateticarum tomi primi libri XIII, etc.
Venetiis, 1571. 4°
C.76.b.5.

F. Patritii Discussionum Peripateticarum tomi IV. Quibus Aristotelicae philosophiae universa historia atque dogmata cum veterum placitis collata, declarantur, etc.
Basiliae, 1581. fol.
525.m.3

See JOHN, of Alexandria, The Grammarian, etc. Expositiones in omnes XIII Aristotelis libros ... quas F. Patricius de Graecis, Latinas fecerat.
1583. fol.
526.m.6.(4.)

See PROCLUS, Diadochus. Procli ... Elementa Theologica et Physica ... Quae F. Patricius de Graecis fecit Latina.
1583. 4°
1010.b.10

Francisci Patricii Apologia contra calumnias J. Angelutii ejusque novae sententiae, quod Metaphysica eadem sint quae Physica
Ferrariae, 1584. 4°
519.d.6.(2.)

F. Patritii Philosophiae de Rerum Natura libri II. priores. Alter de spacio physico, alter de spacio mathematico.
Ferrariae, 1587. 4°
233.f.41

Magia Philosophica: hoc est, F. Patricii ... Zoroaster et ejus 320 Oracula Chaldaica. Asclepii Dialogus & Philosophia magna. Hermetis Trismegisti

Poemander. Sermo Sacer ... et alia Miscellanea ... Latine reddita.
Hamburgi, 1593. 16°
524.a.22
[Another copy] COPIOUS MS. NOTES.
1135.a.2

Nova de Universis Philosophia Libris quinquaginta comprehensa. In qua
Aristotelica methodo ... ad primam causam ascenditur. Deinde nova ...
methodo toto in contemplationem venit divinitas. Postremo methodo
Platonica rerum universitas a conditore Deo deducitur ... Quibus ... sunt
adjecta, Zoroastis oracula CCCXX. Gr. and Lat. Hermetis Trismegisti
libelli, & fragmenta ... Asolepii ... tres libelli. Gr. and Lat. Mystica
AEgyptiorum, a Platone dictata, ab Aristotele excepta, etc. Gr. and Lat.
Venetiis, 1593. fol.
536.l.10

De iis quae sub auditum cadunt, sive de audibilibus [of Aristotle]. Interprete
F. Patricio. See ARISTOTLE. [Works.] Aristoteles ... (Latine, etc.)
1831, etc. 4°
2048.h

Francisci Patricii primae philosophiae liber. In: GARIN (E.) Note su alcuni
aspetti delle retoriche rinascimentali e sulla "Retorica" del Patrizi.
1953. 8°. [Archivio di filosofia. 1953. no. 3.]
Ac.104.df/2

DUDITH, ANDREAS – ANDRIJA DUDIĆ (1533-1589)

Dionysii Halicarnassei de Thucydidis historia judicium, A. Duditio ...
interprete. See DIONYSIUS of Halicarnassus
1560. 4°
585.c.20

Orationes duae in ... Concilio Tridentino habitae.
Venetiis, 1562. 4°
697.d.21.(3)
[Another copy]
222.e.22.(12)

[Another copy] Orationes duae in sacrosancto (Ecumenico Concilio Tridentino habitae, etc.
Venetiis, 1562. 4°
1490.cc.6.(2)
[Another edition]
Brixiae, 1562. 4°
3906.g.35
[Another copy] Orationes duae in sacrosancto (Ecumenico Concilio Tridentino habitae, etc.
Brixiae, 1562. 4°
1492.m.11.(7)

Vita Reginaldi Poli, etc. [Translated from the Italian by A.Dudith.]
See: BECCADELLI, L. successively Bishop of Ravello, etc.
1563. 4°
491.c.10.(1)

Dionysii Halicarnassei de Thucydidis historia judicium, A. Duditio interprete. See BODIN (J.) J. Bodini methodus historica, etc.
1576. 8°
580.c.9

Dionyssi Halicarnassei de Thucydidis historia judicium. A.D. interprete. See WOLFIUS (Joannes) Jurist. Artis historicae penus, etc. tom. 1.
1579. 8°
304.a.5

A. Dudith ... de cometarum significatione Commentariolus. In quo ... mathematicorum quorundam in ea re vanitas refutatur ... Addidimus T. Erasti eadem de re sententia. [Edited by J.M. Brutus]
Basiliae, 1579. 4°
532.e.12.(2)
[Another edition] See ERASTUS (T.) De Cometis Dissertationes Novae, etc.
1580. 4°
532.e.12.(3-6)

M. Celsus de hereticis capitali supplicio non afficiendis. Adjunctae sunt

66

ejusdem argumenti T. Bezae et A.D. epistolae duae contrariae, etc. See: M.
CELSUS
1584. 8°
857.f.5

Epistolarum philosophicarum medicinalium ac chymicarum a summis
nostrae aetatis philosophis ac medicis [i.e. A. Dudith and others] exaratarum,
volumen, etc. See SCHOLZIUS, L.
1598. fol.
545.k.11.(2)

Andrae Dudithii Epistola. See LAVATERUS (Joannes R.) Theologian.
Quaestio vbi vera et catholica Iesu Christi ecclesia invenienda sit, etc.
1610. 8°
847.h.13.(2)

Andrae Dudithii ... Orationes in Concil. Trident. habitae. Apologia ad D.
Maximil. II. Imp. Commentarius pro coniugii libertate. Cum appendice
epistolarum ... Nunc edita studio ac opera D. Quirini Reuteri.
pp. 230. Typis Conradi Nebenii, impensis verò Arpoldi-Philippi Kopffii:
Offenbachi, 1610. 4°
1492.aa.6

De baptismo aquae disputatio Fausti Socini ... Cui accesserunt ejusdem F.
Socini ... Responsiones ad priores & posteriores notas A.D. [i.e. of A.
Dudith] in Disputat. de baptismo, etc. See SOCINUS (F.P.)
1613. 8°
4226.c.12.(2)

De Cometarum significatione cl. virorum A. Duditii commentariolus et D.
Thomae Erasti sententia. Elias Maior ... denuo edidit, et adjecit *paradokson
hoti oudeis kometes, hostis ouk agathon pherei.* [In Greek]
Breslae, 1619. 8°
1607/676

Epistola ad Joannem Cratonem de Significatione Cometarum. See BOSIUS
(J.A.) De Significatu Cometarum, etc.
1665. 4°
532.e.23

[Another edition] See GRAEVIUS (J.G.) J.G. Graevii Oratio de Cometis, etc.
1681. 4°
532.e.25.(15)

Judicium de cometarum significatione. See SERLIN (W.) Cometologia, etc.
1665. 4°
8563.aaa.39

Vita R. Poli, etc [Translated from the Italian of L. Beccadelli, by A. Dudith]
See POLE, R. Cardinal
1690. 8°
701.a.1

**SCALICHIUS, PAULUS von Lika, Count –
PAVAO SKALIĆ (1534-1575)**

Dialogus P. Scalichii de Lika ... de Missa.
Tubingae, 1558. 8°
3906.a.43

Glossa Pauli Scalichii de Lika ... in triginta duos Articulos Canonis Missae ex Apostolo [i.e. extracts from the Epistles of S. Paul].
Apud Iodocum Cortesanum: Romae, 1558. 8°. The imprint is fictitious; the book was printed in Germany.
3906.a.53

Ad invictissimum et augustissimum Principem ... Ferdinandum ... Genealogia, seu de antiquissima Schalichiorum, sive a Scala ... origine, ab anno ... LXXX. usque ad Annum M.D.LXI. Sermo ... Emendatus et auctus. (J.C. Scaligeri oratio in luctu Audecti Caesaris filii.)
pp. 128. [Joannes Daubman: Konigsberg, 1563.] 8°
9917.aaa.4

Pauli principis de la Scala ... miscellaneorum de rerum caussis ... libri septem. Item ... methodas qua homines ... erroribus turbulentis impliciti ad viam veritatis revocandi & ad beatitudinem consequendam promovendi veniant. Contra centurias Evangelicae veritatis, J. Nasi. Deinde oratio de

instauranda Romanae Ecclesiae doctrina, etc.
Coloniae, 1570. 4°
1010.b.9.(1.)

Pauli principis de la Scala ... primi tomi Miscellaneorum de rerum caussis
... effigies ... nimirum, vaticiniorum & imaginum Joachimi Abbatis Florensis
Calabriae, & Anselmi Episcopi Marsichani, super statu summorum
Pontificum Rhomanae Ecclesiae, contra falsam ... & seditiosam cujusdam
Pseudomagi, quae nuper nomine Theophrasti Paracelsi in lucem prodiit,
pseudomagicam expositionem ... explanatio.
Coloniae Agrippinae, 1570. 4°.
1010.b.9.(2.)

Pauli principis de la Scala et Hun, marchionis Veronae, &c. ... Loci
communes theologici, sive pro ecclesia Rhomana eiusque autoritate atq;
religione, aduersus vesaniam Neopistorum, juxta artificium alphabetariae
revolutionis, oratio, etc.
Coloniae, 1571. 4°.
3908.c.66

VRANČIĆ, FAUST, Bishop of Csanád (1551-1617)

Dictionarium quinque nobilissimarum Europae linguarum, Latinae, Italicae,
Germanicae, Dalmatiae & Vngaricae [By F. Verancsics.]
1595. pp. 128. 4°. See DICTIONARIUM
C.33.f.18.(3)

Dictonarivm septem diversarvm lingvarvm, videlicet Latine, Italice,
Dalmatice, Bohemicè, Polonicè, Germanicè, & Vngaricè, vna cum cuiuslibet
linguae registro siue repertorio vernaculo, Singulari studio & industria
collectum a Petro Lodereckero, etc. [Vrančić's "Dictionarium quinque
nobilissimarum Europae linguarum" of 1595, revised and expanded by
Petrus Lodereckerus to include Czech and Polish, with the addition of
indices into Latin for each language.]
Impensis authoris e Typographaeo Ottmariano: Pragae, 1605. Obl. 4°
Cup.403.u.12

Machinae novae ... [Engravings.] Cum declaratione Latina Italica, Hispanica, Gallica et Germanica. 6 pt.
Venetiis, [1616.] fol. The titlepage is engraved.
535.l.16
[Another copy] Machinae novae, etc. [1616].
L.40/66

Dictionarium pentaglottam. Recudi curavit Josephus Thewrewk de Ponor [With a biography of Verancsics by Georgius Gyurikovits.]
Pasonii, 1834. pp. xx. 128. 4°
1333.g.21

GEORGIUS RAGUSEUS - JURAJ DUBROVČANIN (Died 1622)

Georgii Ragusaei ... Peripateticae Disputationes, in quibus difficiliores Naturalis Philosophiae quaestiones examinantur, praecipua obscurioraque Aristotelis loca illustrantur, *etc.*
Venetiis, 1613. fol.
520.k.15

Georgii Ragusaei ... Epistolarum mathematicarum, seu de divinatione libri duo. ... Accessit ejusdem autoris disputatio de puero et puella qui ... Patavii, occasione magni cujusdam incendii, e ruinis extracti, atque ad D. Antonii Confessoris altare delati, revixisse putantur. [Edited by C.H. Fabrotus.]
Parisiis, 1623. 8°
719.c.13

DE DOMINIS, MARKO ANTUN (1560-1624)

De radiis visus et lucis in vitris perspectivis et iride tractatus. Per J. Bartolum in lucem editus Venetiis, 1611. 4°
537.f.28.(1)
[Another copy] De radiis visus et lucis in vitris perspectivis et iride tractatus, etc.
1611.
1608/4569

Marcus Antonius De Dominis ... suae profectionis consilium exponit
Venetiis, 1616. 23p. 8°
C.150.n.12.(6)

M.A. de Dominis ... suae profectionis consilium exponit
Apud J. Billium: Londini, 1616. 4°
491.c.27
[Another copy] MS NOTE. The titlepage is slightly mutilated
1416.f.34
[Another edition] Hagae Comitis, 1616. 4°
477.a.26.(2)
[Another edition] [Leyden?], 1617. 4°
477.a.26.(3)
[Another edition] Epistola Episc. Spalat. M.A. de D. ... in qua causas
discessus à suo Episcopatu exponit
Campidoni, 1617. 4°
3901.d.17

A manifestation of the motives whereupon ... M.A. de Dominis, Archbishop
of Spalatro undertook his departure thence. Englished out of his Latin Copy.
(Decretum sacrae congregationis ... Cardinalium ... ad Indicem Librorum,
... deputatorum publicandum [condemning the work]. The same in English.
A parcell of observations upon ... this Decree. A letter ... to the aforesaid
Archbishop by G. Lingelsheim. Latin and English)
J. Bill, London, 1616. 4°
477.a.26.(1)

A Declaration of the Reasons which moved Marcus Antonius de Dominis,
Archbishop of Spalato or Salonas, Primate of Dalmatia and Croatia, to
depart from the Romish Religion and his Countrey. Written by himselfe in
Latine, and now for the populare use translated [by W.S.]. [With a
woodcut]. MS NOTES. pp. 24.
Andro Hart: Edinburgh, 1617. 4°
C.25.e.1

A Declaration of the Reasons which moved Marcus Antonius de Dominis
to depart from the Romish Religion and his Countrey. Written by himself in
Latin and now ... translated. A Relation sent from Rome of the processe,
sentence, and execution done upon the body, picture and bookes of M.A.D.,

etc. See SOMERS (J) Baron Somers. A Collection of scarce and valuable Tracts, etc. vol. 4.
1748. 4°
184.a.4
[Another edition] See SOMERS (J) Baron Somers. A Collection of scarce ... Tracts, etc. vol. 2.
1809, etc. 4°
750.g.2

Papatus Romanus: liber de origine, progressu, atque extinctione ipsius. [By M.A. de Dominis.]
Londini: ex officina Nortoniana; apud Iohannem Billium, 1617. 206p. 4°
475.b.7.(2)
[Another edition] Francofurti: in officina Godefridi Tampachii, 1618. 178p. 12°
1020.a.12

M.A. de D. sui Reditus ex Anglia consilium exponit.
Romae, 1623. 4°. The imprint on the verso of the last leaf is Lovanii
477.a.26.(10)
[Another edition] Dilingae, 1623. 4°
T.1519.(3)

M.A. de Dominis, ... declares the cause of his Returne, out of England. Translated out of the Latin copy printed at Rome [by Edward Coffin]
St Omar, 1623. pp. 86. 8°
477.a.26.(12)
[Another copy] M. Antonius de Dominis, ... declares the cause of his Returne, out of England, etc.
1623. 8°
C.26.k.8.(2)

My motives for renouncing the Protestant Religion [Translated from the Latin by Dr John Fletcher]
London, 1827. 8°
3936.d.22

De Republica Ecclesiastica Libri x. (Pars secunda ... cum appendicibus ... in quibus ... refellitur opus ... Cardinalis Perronii, in ea Parte in qua agitur de Sanctissima Eucharistia ... Additur ... Responsio ad magnam partem Defensionis Fidei P.F. Suarez. Pars tertia ... Cum ... G. Cassandri tractatu De Officio pii viri circa religionis Dissidia, etc.) 3 pt.
Apud J. Billium, Londini, Francofurti, 1617-58. fol.
477.e.7-9
[Another edition] 3 pt. Heidelbergae, Francofurti ad Moenum, Francofurti, 1618-58. fol.
13.c.11-13

Euripus seu de fluxu et refluxu maris sententia
Romae, 1624. 4°
537.g.39

De Pace Religionis ... epistola ad Josephum Hallum ... in qua sui etiam ex Anglia proximi discessus rationem reddit ... et ab ipso Hallo increpationes acceptas rejicit
Vesuntione Sequanorum, 1666. 4°
477.a.26.(16)

[M.A. de Dominis sui reditus ex Anglia consilium exponit.] The second manifesto of Marcus Antonius de Dominis ... wherein for his better satisfaction, and the satisfaction of others, he publikley repenteth, and recanteth his former errors, and setteth downe the cause of his leauing England, and all Protestant countries, to returne vnto the Catholicke Romane Church ... translated into English by M.G.K. In: English Recusant literature, etc. vol. 128.
1973. A facsimile of the edition of 1623, printed at Liège by Guillaume Hovius. Made from a copy in the library of Downside Abbey.
1564/128

Supplicatio ad Imperatorem, reges, principes, super causis generalis Concilij convocandi. Contra Paulum Quintum. [The dedication signed: Novus Homo. By M.A. de Dominis?] pp. 30.
Bonham Norton, Londini, 1513 [1613]. 4° See PAUL V., Pope [Camillo Borghese]
3935.bb.1

SANCTORIUS, SANCTORIUS (1561-1636)

De remediorum inventione. *See* HIPPOCRATES. S. Sanctorii ...
commentaria in primam sectionem aphorismorum Hippocratis, *etc.*
1629. 4°
539.f.16.(1.)

Methodi vitandorum errorum omnium, qui in arte medica contingunt libri
quindecim ... Multa in hac nova editione ab ipso auctore addita & emendata.
col. 972. *Apud M.A. Brogiollum: Venetiis*, 1630. 4°
539.f.16.(2.)

S. Sanctorii de Medicina Statica aphorismi. Commentaria, notasque addidit
A.C. Lorry.
Parisiis, 1770. 12°
1039.d.24

KASSICH, BARTOLOMEO – BARTOL KAŠIĆ (1575-1650)

Institutionum linguae Illyricae Libri duo.
Roma, 1604. 8°
236.e.26

FERCHIUS, MATTHAEUS – MATE FRKIĆ (1583-1669)

Istri seu Danubii aliorumque fluminum ab Aristotele in primo Meteoro
inductorum. Accessit Lacus Asphaltitis confirmatio.
Patavii, 1632. 4°
445.b.30.(4)

De Personis producentibus Spiritum Sanctum, etc.
Patavii, [1644?] 4°
1010.d.8.(2)

De Caelesti substantia et ejus ortu ac motu in sententia Anaxagorae.
(Anaxagorae vita.) [Edited by P.M. Rusca]
Venetiis, 1646. 4°
520.c.15

Defensio Vestigationum Peripateticum M.F. ... ab offensionibus Belluti et
Mastrii.
[Edited by J. Georgius.] Patavii, 1646. 4°
527.i.16

Epitome theologicum M.F. Veglensis ... ex Magistro Sententiarum [i.e.
Petrus Lombardus] et ... Jo. [Duns] Scoto, a M.P.M. Rusca ... evulgatum.
pp. 277, 255, 201, 296. Patavii, 1647. 8°
3554.cc.13

LUCIUS, JOANNES - IVAN LUČIĆ (1604-1679)

See BUDÉ (G.) Forensium verborum et loquendi generum, quae sunt a G.B.
proprio commentario descripta, Gallica de foro Parisiensi sumpta
interpretatio, etc. [Edited by G. Lucio]
1545. fol.
16.c.7.(2)

J. Lucii de regno Dalmatiae et Croatiae libri sex. (Presbyteri Diocleatis
regnum Slavorum. -Regnum Dalmatiae et Croatiae gesta ... a M. Marulo ...
Latinitate donata. -Thomae Archidiaconi Spalatensis Historia Salonitanorum
Pontificum atque Spalatensium. -M. Madii Historia Spalaten. -Tabula
Historiarum a Catheis de gestis civium Spalaten. - Memoria Archi-
episcoporum Salonitae, et Spalatinae Ecclesiae. -Obsidionis Jadrensis libri
duo Memoriale Pauli de Paulo Patritii Jadrensis. -J. Lucii Notae ad eosdem.
-P. Fusci ... de situ orae Illyrici liber primus (-secundus). -M. Marulli ... In
eos qui ... Hieronymum Italum esse contendunt [liber]. -Appiani Alexandrini
... Hist. de bellis Illyricis, etc.)
pp. 474. J. Blaeu: Amstelaedami, 1666. fol.
149.f.4
[Another copy] J. Lucii de regno Dalmatiae et Croatiae libri sex.
J. Blaeu: Amstelodami, 1668. fol. Another copy of the preceding, with a
new titlepage and preliminary matter, and with the addition of an index.

Imperfect; wanting all after page 370.
590.i.22
[Another edition] See SCHWANDTNERUS (J.G.) Scriptores Rerum
Hungaricarum veteres, etc. tom III.
1746, etc. fol.
149.g.3

J. Lucii Inscroiptiones Dalmaticae. Notae ad Memoriale Pauli de Paulo.
Notae ad Palladium Fuscum. Addenda, vel corrigenda in opere di regno
Dalmatiae et Croatiae. Variae lectiones chronici Ungarici manuscripti cum
editis.
Typis S. Curtii: Venetiis, 1673. 4°
590.g.19.(2)
[Another copy]
794.g.28
[Another copy]
661.d.22
[Another copy]
661.c.11.(2)
[Another copy]
661.c.12.(2)
[Another edition] See DALMATIA. Alter und neuer Staat des Königreichs
Dalmatien, etc.
1718. 8°
10291.a.21

Editio nova atque emendata
Vindobonae, 1758. fol.
799.m.5

RATTKAY, GEORGIUS, Baron de Nagy Thabor –
JURAJ RATKAJ, barun Velikotaborski (1612-1666)

Memoria Regum et Banorum Regnorum Dalmatiae Croatiae et Sclavoniae
... usque ad praesentem annum M.DC.LII. deducta
Viennae Austriae, 1653. fol.
149.d.1.

76

Editio altera ... Mariae Theresiae Augustae dicata ab A. Semsey de Eadem
Viennae, 1772. 4°
C.130.c.11

GRADI, STEFANO – STJEPAN GRADIĆ (1613-1683)

Poemata Stephani Gradii, etc. In: VIRI. Septem illustrium virorum poemata.
pp. 229-244. 1662. 8°
11409.l.45
[Another edition] 1672. 8°
11405.d.49

See VIDA (Marcus Hieronymus) Bishop of Alba. Christiade, etc. (De vita,
ingenio, et studiis Auctoris [i.e. G. Palmotić] S. Gradius)
V Rimu, 1670. 4°
C.136.bb.1

Stephani Gradii ... de laudibus Serenissimae Reipublicae Venetae et cladibus
Patriae suae Carmen.
pp. 24. Franciscus Valuasenis: Venetiis, 1675. 4°
11409.gg.40.(6)

In Funere Caesaris Rasponi S.R.E. Cardinalis Oratio.
pp. 33
Franciscus Tizzoni: Romae, 1676. 4°
11409.gg.40.(7)

S. Gradii ... Disputatio de opinione probabili. cum H. Fabri.
Romae, 1678. 4°
475.a.7
[Another edition] Romae, 1689. 8°
748.c.12

Stephani Gradii ... Disputatio de opinione probabili cum P. Honorato Fabri,
etc.
Mechliniae: Gisber. Lintsius, 1679. pp.225 8°
848.c.12

S.G. ... Dissertationes physico-mathematicae quatuor.
Amstlodami, 1680. 8°
536.b.15.(2)

Appiani Alexandrini Romanarum Historiarum de Bellis Illyricis Liber S.G.
... interprete. See SCHWANDTNERUS (J.G.) Scriptores rerum
Hungaricarum, etc. tom. 3.
1746, etc. fol.
149.g.3

See CERVARIUS TUBERO (L.) Commentariolus ... de origine et
incremento Urbis Rhacusanae, ... et S.G. antiquitatum Rhacusanarum
diatriba, etc.
1790. 4°
665.d.3

Le tre descrizioni del terremoto de Ragusa del 1667 di Gradi, Rogacci, Stay.
Versione dal Latino [by Luca Stulli]. [In verse.]
pp. 62. Venezia, 1828. 8°
11426.cc.15.(6)

Leonis Allatii vita. In: MAI (A.) Cardinal. Patrum nova Biblioteca. tom. 6.
1852, etc. 4°
3623.d.3

PASTRITIUS, JOANNES - PAŠTRIĆ, IVAN (1636-1708)

Patenae Argenteae Mysticae quae ... Divi Petri Chrysologi ... Ravennatis
Archiepiscopi munus, Foro-Cornelii in Cathedrali Ecclesia Sancti Cassiani
Martyris colitur, descriptio, et explicato, etc.
Romae, 1706. 4°
660.f.11
[Another copy]
860.l.22

NICOLAUS PLUMBEUS, BISHOP OF BOSNIA
OGRAMIĆ-OLOVČIĆ, NIKOLA (1639-1701)

Opusculum vitae, virtutum et miraculorum ... Fr. Sebastiani ab Apparitio, authore Fratre Nicolao Plumbensi, Diacovensi ... Episcopo ... Innocentio Papae XII. litatum. Cura, ac solicitudine R.P.F. Joannis Fernandez Zejudo, *etc.* pp.207
Ex Officina Camerae Apostolicae: Romae, 1696. 4°
1372.i.14

RITTER, PAULUS-VITEZOVIĆ (1652-1713)

Stemmatographia, sive armorum Illyricorum delineatio, descriptio et restitutio
[Vienna? 1701?] 4°
11403.b.45

RESTIUS, JUNIUS – DŽONO ANTUNOV RASTIĆ (1669-1735)

Chronica Ragusini Junii Restii, ab origine urbis usque ad annum 1451, item J. Gundulae 1451-1484. Digessit N. Nodilo.
pp. xix. 439. 1893. See ZAGREB. JAZU. SOUTH SLAVONIANS. Monumenta, etc. vol. 25. 1868, etc. 8°
Ac.741/3

BANDURI, ANSELMO (1675-1743)

Imperium orientale, sive Antiquitates Constantinopolitanae, in quatuor partes distributae: quae ex variis scriptorum graecorum operibus & praesertim ineditis adornatae, commentariis, & geographicis, topographicis, aliisque ... tabellis illustrantur ... Operâ & studio Domni A. Bandurii. [With plates]
Parisiis, 1711. pp. 1016. 14*. fol.
578.m.22
[Another edition] 2 tom. 1729. See BYZANTINE HISTORY. Corpus Byzantinae historiae, etc.
1729, etc. fol.

804.i.2/15
[Another copy]
195.h.9

Numismata imperatorum Romanorum à Trajano Decio ad Palaeologos Augustos. Accessit bibliotheca nummaria sive auctorum qui de re nummaria scripserunt. [With plates.] 2 tom.
Lutetiae Parisiorum, 1718. fol.
677.k.6
[Another copy.] L.P.
139.g.1,2

D. Anselmi Bandurii Bibliotheca nummaria, sive auctorum qui de re nummaria scripserunt ... cum notulis et indicibus recusa, curante Io. Alberto Fabricio.
Hamburgi, 1719. pp. 248. 4°
270.k.41

Numismatum imperatorum Romanorum à Trajano Decio ad Constatinum Draconem ab A. Bandurio editorum supplementum, confectum studio et curâ Hieronymi Taninii.
Romae, 1741. pp. xv. 458. pl. XII. fol.
677.k.7
[Another copy]
139.g.3

Anselmii Bandurii In scriptores anonymi de antiquitatibus Cpolitanis librum IV, ubi de aede Sophiana, commentarius. [Extracted from the author's "Imperium orientale"] 1837. See BYZANTINE HISTORY. Corpus scriptorum historiae Byzantinae. pt. 19.
1828, etc. 8°
2071.h.19

Animadversiones in Constantini Porphyrogeniti libros de thematibus et de administrando imperio. [Extracted from the author's "Imperium orientale"] 1840. 8°. See CONSTANTINE VII. Emperor of the East. De thematibus, etc. [Corpus scriptorum historiae Byzantinae. pt. 5. vol. 3]
2071.g.5

Anselmi Bandurii ad Nicephori Callisti catalogum observationes et notae. [Extracted from the author's "Imperium orientale"] 1865. See MIGNE (J.P.) Patrologiae cursus completus, etc. Series Graeca. tom. 147. 1857, etc. 4°
2002.b

ĐURĐEVIĆ, IGNJAT, Abbot of Mljet [Nikola Đurđević] – GEORGIUS IGNATIUS (1675-1737)

D. Paulus Apostolus in Mari, quod nunc Venetus Sinus dicitur, naufragus, et Melitae Dalmatensis Insulae post naufragium hospes, sive, De genuino significatu duorum locorum in Actibus Apostolicis ... Adjicitur brevis dissertatio ejusdem autoris de catellis Melitaeis. [With maps.] Venetiis, 1730. pp. cccxii. 4°
661.e.12

Latinske pjesni razlike (Poetici Iusus varii) Zagreb, JAZU, 1956. pp. XXXIII 297. 8°. In: Hrvatski Latinisti, Knjiga 4 Ac.741/31(4)

Rerum Illyricarum Ignjata Đurđevića, etc. [Edited, with notes, by Ivan Pudić. With a portrait and facsimiles, and with a bibliography.] Sarajevo, 1967. 8°. [Akademija nauka i umjetnosti Bosne i Hercegovine. Djela. knj. 28. Odjeljenje istorijsko-filoloških nauka. knj. 16.] Ac.9233.of

Homerum nunquam fuisse suspicio. Za štampu priredila Darinka Nevenić-Grabovac, etc. [With a facsimile and a summary in French.] Beograd, 1968. pp. 62. 8°. [In: SANU. Posebna izdanja Knj. 420. Odelenje literatutre i jezika, Knj. 19.] Ac.1131

BABIĆ, TOMA (c.1680-1750)

Prima grammaticae institutio pro tyronibus Illyricis accomodata ... In hac secunda impressione clarior et difusior. pp.448 *Venetiis*, 1745. 8°
1568/4170

LASTRIĆ, FILIP (1700-1783)

Philippus, ab Occhievia.

Epitome vetustatum Bosniensis provinciae, seu Brevissimum compendium historico-chronologicum de antiquitate, variisque suis vicissitudinibus, et consistentia usque ad haec tempora. Locupletata in hac nova editione nonnullis additionibus ... Congesta, et compilata a P. Philippo ab Occhievia, etc. pp. XII.134. Anconae, 1776. 4°.
09136.g.1

Testimonium bilabium, seu Sermones panegyrico-dogmatico-morales ... latine, & illyrice elaborati, ad honorem & gloriam, atque in obsequium SS. Nominis ... Jesus; 2 pt. pp. 398. 144. Venetiis, 1755. 4°.
1485.r.4

BOSCOVICH, RUGGIERO GIUSEPPE – JOSIP RUĐER BOŠKOVIĆ (1711-1787)

Problema mecanicum de solido maximae attractionis solutum, etc. [With a diagram.] See GIULIANI (C.A.) Memorie sopra la fisica e istoria naturale, etc. tom. 1.
1743, etc. 8°
957.i.1

Dissertatio de telluris figura ... nunc primum aucta, & illustrata, etc. 1744. See GIULIANI (C.A.) Memorie sopra la fisica e istoria naturale, etc. tom. 2.
1743, etc. 8°
957.i.2

Nova methodus adhibendi phasium observationes in eclipsibus lunaribus ... dissertatio, etc. [With a diagram] 1747. See GIULIANI (C.A.) Memorie sopra la fisica e istoria naturale, etc. tom. 3.
1743, etc. 8°
957.i.2

Dissertatio de maris aestu.

Romae, 1747. pp. lvi. 4°
8775.e.19.(1)

De centro gravitatis dissertatio ... Editio altera. Accedit disquisitio in centrum magnitudinis, qua quaedam in ea dissertatione proposita ... demonstrantur.
pp. lvi. pl. II. Romae, 1751. 4°
8775.e.19.(2)

De lunae atmosphaera dissertatio [With a diagram]
pp. lxxv. Romae, 1753. 4°
705.g.5.(2)
[Another edition] Dissertatio de lunae atmosphaera.
pp. lll. [Vienna? 1770?] 4°
8560.e.15.(2)

De continuitatis lege et ejus consectariis pertinentibus ad prima materiae elementa eorumque vires dissertatio, etc.
pp. 80. Romae, 1754. 4°
8704.f.12.(2)
[Another copy]
705.g.5.(1)

De lentibus et telescopiis dioptricis dissertatio. [With a diagram.]
pp. 58. Romae, 1755. 4°
537.k.24

[Latin poems] 1756. See MOREI (M.G.) Arcadum carmina. pt. 2. 1757, etc.
8°
78.c.34

De materiae divisibilitate et principiis corporum dissertatio ... nunc primum edita. 1757. See GIULIANI (C.A.) Memorie sopra la fisica e istoria naturale, etc. tom. 4.
1743, etc. 8°
957.i.1,2

Elementorum universae matheseos ... tomus I (II) ... Editio prima Veneta ... ab erroribus expurgata. [With diagrams] 2 tom.
Venetiis, 1757. 8°
60.a.25

Theoria micrometri objectivi, etc. In: Clarissimi viri D. de La Caille ... Lectiones elementares opticae, etc.
1757. pp. 143-150. 4°
1601/536

De solis ac lunae defectibus libri v ... Editio Veneta prima ex exemplari editionis Londiniensis anni 1760. Correcto, et perpolito ab ipso auctore. Venetiis: Typis Antonii Zatta, 1761. pp. xliii, 343. 8°.
1608/4750

Trigonometria plana, et sphaerica. In: EUCLID. [Elementa] Elementa geometriae, etc. pp. 252-327
1761. 8°
1394.b.15

Dissertationes quinque ad dioptricam pertinentes
Vindobonae, 1767. pp. 290. pl. III. 4°
537.k.26

[De solis ac lunae defectibus] Les Eclipses, poëme en six chants ... Traduit en françois par M. l'abbé de Barruel. Latin and French.
pp. xxxii. 540. Paris, 1779. 4°
640.k.11

Nouveaux ouvrages de Monsieur l'abbé Boscovich appartenants principalement à l'optique et à l'astronomie, etc. (Rogerii Josephi Boscovich opera pertinentia ad opticam, et astronomiam, etc.) Latin and French. 5 tom.
Bassan, 1785. 4°
50.d.3

[Theoria philosophiae naturalis] A Theory of Natural Philosophy ... Latin-English edition from ... the first Venetian edition ... 1763. With a short life of Boscovich. [Edited by Branislav Petronijević. Translated by J.M. Child. With a catalogue of the works of R.G. Boscovich]

Chicago, London; Open Court Publishing Co. Frome printed 1922. pp. xix. 463. fol.
8464.h.3

O prostoru, vremenu i relativnosti. Predgovor, izbor tekstova i prevod Dr. Dušana Nedeljkovića. [With the original text and a portrait] Beograd, 1956. pp. 64. 8°. Part of the "Mala filozofska biblioteka"
8477.y.77

BENEDICTUS STAY – BENEDIKT STAY-STOJKOVIĆ (1714-1801)

Philosophiae ... versibus traditae libri sex. Editio secunda auctior, etc. Romae, 1747. 8°. The date of the colophon is 1748.
528.f.39

Philosophiae recentioris ... versibus traditae libri x. Cum adnotationibus et supplementis ... R.J. Boscovich. 2 tom. Romae, 1755-60. 8°
78.e.22.
[Another edition] Romae, 1792. 8°
11405.f.29

Oratio in funere Clementis XIII. Pontificis Maximi. Romae, 1769. 4°
T.40*.(9.)

BALTHASAR ADAM KERCSELICH de Corbavia (1715-1778)

Historiarum Cathedralis ecclesiae Zagrabiensis Partis Primae tomus 1 ... continens seriem episcoporum ab anno 1091 ad annum 1603 et tam episcoporum quam et alias notitias, etc. tom. 1. Zagrabiae, [1770.] fol. No more published
4630.e.10

85

De Regnis Dalmatiae, Croatiae, Sclavoniae, notitiae preliminares, etc.
Zagrabiae, [1771.] fol.
9325.g.6
[Another copy] De Regnis Dalmatiae, Croatiae, Sclavoniae, notitiae
preliminares, etc.
[1771.] 8°. Wanting the dedication to the Empress Maria Theresa
1489.m.9

Annuae, ili Historija, 1748-1767 (Annuae sive Historia ad Posteritatis
notitiam. Urednik Nikola Majnarić, Preveo Veljko Gortan) [With the funeral
oration by Vinko Kalafatić]
Zagreb, 1952. pp. 630. fol.
In: Hrvatski Latinisti, Knjiga 3
Ac.741/31(3)

PAVIĆ, MIRKO EMERIK (1716-1780)

[Razgovor ugodni naroda slovinskoga.] Descriptio soluta et rythmica regum,
banorum, caeterorumque heroum Slavinorum seu Illyricorum ... in vernacula
lingua Illyrica proposita, recenter perbrevi compilatione in Latinum traducta
... a P. Emerico a Buda ... praefixa notitia imperatorum ... atque eximiorum
Dei servorum gentis praelibatae. [Preceded by 2 leaves, with a titlepage
commencing as the above, containing "Assertiones de Deo Uno ... ex
praelectionibus patris Hyacinthi Campion," etc.] pp. 190.
Budae, 1764. 4°
9475.b.9

See GREGORIUS [Čevapović], Franciscan.
Synoptico-memorialis catalogus Observantis Minorum Provinciae S.
Joannis, a Capistrano ...
1823. 8°
4785.dd.1

CUNICHIUS, RAYMUNDUS– RAJMUND KUNIĆ (1719-1794)

Clemente XIII. Pontifice Maximo renunciato. Oratio habita in Collegio
Romano Prid. Kal. Sept. CIO IO CCLVIII.

Romae, 1758. pp. xxiii. 4°
T.43*.(11)

Rogero Boscovichio ... Romam redeunte elegia P. Raymundi Cunichii, etc.
Tyrnaviae, 1763. pp. 12. 4°
11408.bb.66.(3)

Raymundi Cunich ... Elegiae XIV ... hactenus ineditae ... Edente Crisauro
Philomuso Arcadiae Pastore. See SZYMONOWICZ (S.) Bendonski.
Poetarum elegiographorum par nobile, Simon Simonides ... Raymundus
Cunich, etc.
1771. 4°
837.g.40.(1)

See HOMER. [Iliad. -Latin] Homeri Ilias Latinis versibus expressa a R.
Cunichio, etc.
1776. fol.
71.h.2

See THEOCRITUS. [Latin] Thaeocriti Idyllia et epigrammata Latine
conversa a R. Cunichio, etc.
1799. 8°
11335.g.10

Raymundi Cunichii Ragusini Epigrammata, nunc primum in lucem edita.
[Edited by Raffaele Radeglia]
Ragusii, 1827. pp. iv. 340. vii. 8°
11409.cc.21

See HOMER. [Iliad. – Polyglot] Homeri Ilias Graece, quam vertebant Latine
soluta oratione C.G. Heyne, versibus item Latinis R. Cunich, etc.
1837. 4°
652.d.5,6

87

MICHELAZZI, AUGUSTIN (1732-1820)

Compendium regni vegetabilis, *etc.* pp. xiv. 294.
[Gorizia, 1776.] 8°
449.e.33

Compendium regni fossilium
Goritiae, 1781. 8°
970.g.2

MIKOCZY, JOSIP (1734-1800)

Otiorum Croatiae liber unus, etc.
Budae, 1806. pp.xvi, 447. 21cm.
1568/4532

ZAMAGNA, BERNARDUS– BRNO DŽAMANJIĆ (1735-1820)

B. Zamagna ... Echo: Libri duo. Selecta Graecorum Carmina versa Latine
a R. Cunichio.
Romae, 1764. 8°
237.k.9

Homeri Odyssea Latinis versibus expressa a B. Zamagna. See HOMER
[Odysseia.]
1777. fol.
71.h.1.

Hesiodi opera ... Latinis versibus expressa ... a B.Zamagna. See HESIOD
[Works.]
1785. 4°
53.f.2

Hesiodi opera omnia Latinis versibus expressa, atque illustrata a B.
Zamagna, etc. See HESIOD [Works.]
1797. 4°
653.d.5

Carmina [On the occasion of the Peace of 1814.]
[Ragusa], 1814. 4°
11409.gg.40.(8)

Navis aeria of B. Zamagna. Translation by Mary B. McElwain, etc.
pp. viii. 123. Northampton, Mass., 1939. 8°. [Smith College Classical
Studies. no. 12.]
Ac.1877

FERIĆ, JURO (1739-1820)

Ad clarissimum virum Julium Bajamontium ... epistola. [In verse.]
pp. 24. Ragusii, 1799. 8°
899.cc.4.(9)

Periegesis orae Rhacusanae, duobus libris comprehensa. [In verse.]
pp. 176. Rhacusii, 1803. 8°
11405.c.22

Ad clarissimum virum Michaelem Denisium ... epistola. [In verse.]
pp. 20. Ragusii, 1824. 8°
899.cc.4.(10)

KATANČIĆ, MATIJA PETAR (1750-1825)

Specimen philologiae et geographiae Pannoniorum in quo de origine, lingua
et literatura Croatorum, simul de Sisciae Andautonii, Nevioduni,
Poetovionis, urbium in Pannonia olim celebrium ... situ disseritur.
pp. 228. Zagrabiae, 1795. 4°
12976.i.41

Orbis antiquus ex tabula itineraria quae Theodosii Imp. et Peutingeri audit
ad systema geographiae redactus et commentario illustratus. 2 pt.
Budae, 1824, 25. 4°
10004.k.11

DOMIN, JOSIP FRANJO (1754-1819)

DOMIN, Josephus Franciscus
Dissertatio physica.
Iaurini: Typis Iosephi Streibig, 1784. 8°
RB.23.a.1403

PASKVIĆ, IVAN (1754-1829)

Opuscula statico-mechanica principiis analyseos finitorum superstructa.
Cum figuris.
Lipsiae, 1799. 4°
717.h.19

Epitome elementorum Astronomiae sphaerico-calculatoriae. (Appendix ...
complectens tabulas auxiliares.) 3 pt.
Viennae, 1811. 4°
8560.e.1

Tabulae logarithmico-trigonometricae contractae cum novis accessionibus
ad abbreviandos facilioresque redendos calculos trigonometricos.
Abgekürtze logarithmisch-trigonometrische Tafeln. *Latin and German*
Leipzig, 1817. 8°
1394.i.15
[Another copy]
1392.h.14

MARTINOVIĆ, IGNJAT (1755-1795)

Status regni Hungariæ, anno 1792. [By I.J. Martinovics.]
pp.32 [1792] 12°. See HUNGARY. - [Appendix. Political]
8233.a.63.(2.)

WOLFSTEIN, JOSIP (1776-1859)

J.W. ... Introductio in Teoriam Motus.
Cassoviae, 1809. 8°
8530.aa.11

ČEVAPOVIĆ, GRGUR (1786-1830)

Recensio Observantis Minorum Provinciae S. Joann. a Capistrano, per Hung., Austr. Inf., et Slavon. extensae: comentariis ethnol., philol., statist. geogr., hist., illustrata. Cum ... mappa ... pro anno Dom. 1830. [The Approbario Censurae names as author: Gr. Csvopovich.]
pp.666. *Budae*, [1830] 8°
4784.dd.18

Synoptico-memorialis catalogus Observantis Minorum Provinciae S. Joannis, a Capistrano, olim Bosnae Argentinae; a dimidio seculi XIII. usque recentem aetatem, ex archivo et chronicis ejusdem recusus [for the most part from E. Pavich's "Chronicon Observantis Minorum Provinciae Capistranae"]. *Budae*, 1823. 8°
4785.dd.1

SCHROTT, JOSIP (1791-1857)

Ad calendas Novembris MDCCCXII. Croatia Trans-Savana et Litorali Hungarico benignitate ... imperatoris ... Francisci I. sub auspicio ... comitis Josephi Mailáth ... qua ... Regni Hungariae Coronae reunitis devote offert J. Schrott. pp. 7.
Zagrabiae, [1822] 4°
Hung.l.n.16.(17.)

VISIANI, ROBERT (1800-1878)

Stirpium Dalmaticarum Specimen. 2 pt.
Patavii, 1826. 4°
442.g.17

Flora Dalmatica sive enumeratio stirpium vascularium quas hactenus in Dalmatia lectas et sibi observatas descripsit, digessit, rariorumquae iconibus illustravit R. de V. 3 vol.
Lipsiae, 1842-52. 4°. *Vol. 3 is in 2 pt.*
780.k.30

Florae Dalmaticae Supplementum. Opus suum novis curis castigante et augente ... R. de V. (Supplementum alterum, adjectis plantis in Bosnia, Hercegovina et Montenegro crescentibus, etc.)
Venetiis, 1872. *etc.* 4°
7028.g.2

GOLDSCHMIDT (ZLATAROVIĆ), JOSIP (1807-1874)

De aneurysmate cirsoideo et anastomotico. Dissertatio, etc.
Vratislaviae, [*1864*] 8°
7385.e.(5.)

SCHLOSSER, JOSIP (1818-1882) &
LJUDEVIT FARKAŠ VUKOTINOVIĆ (1813-1893)

Syllabus Florae Croaticae additis descriptionibus specierum novarum.
[*Agram*] 1857. 16°
7032.b.56

Flora Croatica exhibens stirpes phanerogamas et vasculares cryptogamas quae in Croatia Slavonia et Dalmatia sponte crescunt nec non illas quae frequentissime coluntur, etc. pp. cxli. 1362
Zagrabiae, 1869. 8°
07031.h.6

SMERDEL, TON (1904-1970)

Pontes lucentes. Carmina Latina.
Zagrebiæ, 1962. pp.42. 8°.
11566.a.10.